Resequencing the Middle Ages through Archaeogenetics

DEBATES IN ARCHAEOLOGY

Series editor: Richard Hodges

Against Cultural Property, John Carman

The Anthropology of Hunter-Gatherers, Vicki Cummings

Archaeologies of Conflict, John Carman

Archaeology: The Conceptual Challenge, Timothy Insoll

Archaeology and International Development in Africa, Colin Breen and Daniel Rhodes

Archaeology and State Theory, Bruce Routledge

Archaeology and Text, John Moreland

Archaeology and the Pan-European Romanesque, Tadhg O'Keeffe

Beyond Celts, Germans and Scythians, Peter S. Wells

Bronze Age Textiles, Klavs Randsborg

Building Colonialism, Daniel T. Rhodes

The Byzantine Dark Ages, Michael J. Decker

Changing Natures, Bill Finlayson and Graeme M. Warren

Combat Archaeology, John Schofield

Debating the Archaeological Heritage, Robin Skeates

Early European Castles, Oliver H. Creighton

Early Islamic North Africa: A New Perspective, Corisande Fenwick

Early Islamic Syria, Alan Walmsley

Empowering Communities through Archaeology and Heritage, Peter G. Gould

Ethics and Burial Archaeology, Duncan Sayer

Evidential Reasoning in Archaeology, Robert Chapman and Alison Wylie

Fishing and Shipwreck Heritage, Sean A. Kingsley

Fluid Pasts, Matthew Edgeworth

From Stonehenge to Mycenae: The Challenges of Archaeological Interpretation, John C. Barrett and Michael J. Boyd

Gerasa and the Decapolis, David Kennedy

Heritage, Communities and Archaeology, Laurajane Smith and Emma Waterton

Houses and Society in the Later Roman Empire, Kim Bowes

Image and Response in Early Europe, Peter S. Wells

Indo-Roman Trade, Roberta Tomber

Islamization and Archaeology: Religion, Culture and New Materialism, José C. Carvajal López

Loot, Legitimacy and Ownership, Colin Renfrew

Lost Civilization, James L. Boone

The Materiality of Ancient Greek Identities, 9th to 2nd Centuries BCE, Emma Gooch and Jerome Ruddick

Museums and the Construction of Disciplines, Christopher Whitehead

Negotiating Migrations: The Archaeology and Politics of Mobility, Daniela Hofmann, Catherine J. Frieman, Martin Furholt, Stefan Burmeister and Niels Nørkjær Johannsen

The Origins of Anglo-Saxon Towns: A Viking Gift, Richard Hodges

The Origins of the Civilization of Angkor, Charles F. W. Higham

The Origins of the English, Catherine Hills

Pagan and Christian, David Petts

The Remembered Land, Jim Leary

Rethinking Wetland Archaeology, Robert Van de Noort and Aidan O'Sullivan

The Roman Countryside, Stephen L. Dyson

Roman Reflections, Klavs Randsborg

Shaky Ground, Elizabeth Marlowe

Shipwreck Archaeology of the Holy Land, Sean A. Kingsley

Social Evolution, Mark Pluciennik

The State in Ancient Egypt: Power, Challenges and Dynamics, Juan Carlos Moreno Garcia

State Formation in Early China, Li Liu and Xingcan Chen

Towns and Trade in the Age of Charlemagne, Richard Hodges

Tradition and Transformation in Anglo-Saxon England, Susan Oosthuizen

Vessels of Influence, Nicole Coolidge Rousmaniere

Villa to Village, Riccardo Francovich and Richard Hodges

Resequencing the Middle Ages through Archaeogenetics

Interpreting the Past through Science and History

Patrick J. Geary

BLOOMSBURY ACADEMIC
LONDON • NEW YORK • OXFORD • NEW DELHI • SYDNEY

BLOOMSBURY ACADEMIC
Bloomsbury Publishing Plc, 50 Bedford Square, London, WC1B 3DP, UK
Bloomsbury Publishing Inc, 1359 Broadway, New York, NY 10018, USA
Bloomsbury Publishing Ireland, 29 Earlsfort Terrace, Dublin 2, D02 AY28, Ireland

First published in Great Britain 2026

Cover design: Holly Capper
Cover image © Yuichiro Chino/Getty Images

A catalogue record for this book is available from the British Library.

A catalog record for this book is available from the Library of Congress.

ISBN: HB: 978-1-3506-1465-9
PB: 978-1-3506-1461-1
ePDF: 978-1-3506-1462-8
eBook: 978-1-3506-1463-5

Series: Debates in Archaeology

Typeset by RefineCatch Limited, Bungay, Suffolk
Printed and bound in Great Britain

For product safety related questions contact productsafety@bloomsbury.com.

For Herwig Wolfram, Mentor, Colleague, Friend,
and Inspiration,
who first introduced me the world of Late Antiquity
and the early Middle Ages

CONTENTS

FIGURES

ACKNOWLEDGEMENTS

This short book draws on a number of previous publications as well as on the expertise of many colleagues with whom I have had the pleasure to work and from whom I have learned a great deal over the past decade. In part, the earlier portions are an expansion of my *Herausforderungen und Gefahren der Integration von Genomdaten in die Erforschung der frühmittelalterlichen Geschichte*, Das Mittelalterliche Jahrtausend Vol. 7 Berlin: Wallterstein Verlag, 2021. I am grateful to Jörg Feuchter and his colleagues at the Berlin-Brandenburg Academy of Sciences for having given me the opportunity to reuse and expand on this publication. The discussion of Sequence Alignment Maps is taken from my article, 'La femme de la tombe 087 à Collegno: La paléogénomique au service de l'histoire d'une communauté en Italie lombarde,' which will appear in the *Mémoires de la Société nationale des antiquaires de France*.

Especially, I wish to acknowledge all that I have been taught by my colleagues in the ERC funded project HistoGenes (grant agreement number 856453 ERC-2019-SyG). These include in the first instance Krishna Veeramah, Johannes Krause, Deven Vyas, Joscha Gretzinger, Zuzana Hofmanová, Alexander Herbig, and Yijie Tian for sharing their extraordinary knowledge of ancient DNA and population genetics. Archaeologists, principally István Koncz, but also Tividar Vida, Falko Daim and Bendeguz Tobias, have been generous with their deep expertise in the study of the material culture of the Carpathian Basin. The historian Walter Pohl has been, throughout this project but indeed throughout most of my career, a wonderful colleague, guide, and critic. Michael Maas and Helmut Reimitz have given me valuable advice on the completed draft. Brett Stephens has worked diligently with me on editing and revising.

This book is an attempt to synthesize what I have learned from these and many more scientists and scholars. Their capacity to teach me has only been limited by my ability to learn from them, and the remaining errors and omissions are entirely my fault.

Introduction: The Genetic Revolution

From the Neanderthals to Denisovans to 23andMe and AncestryDNA, genetics have become the focus of everyone from amateur genealogists looking for their relatives to the Nobel Assembly at Karolinska Institutet that awarded Svante Pääbo the Nobel Prize for his work on ancient DNA. Some of this is fashion; some is hype; and some is dangerous.[1] But when one clears away the exaggerations and clarifies the risks, genetic research truly is transforming how we understand the deep past, the more recent past and ourselves. Medieval history, like prehistory, will never be the same again.

Macrocosm and microcosm

A tsunami of stunning developments in palaeontology and especially ancient DNA studies is radically changing the big picture of the past and the future of the human race. Geneticists have begun to piece together a picture of human evolution that is far more complex than anyone knew even a decade ago. The emergence of modern humans, *Homo sapiens*, and their spread across the globe happened in fits and starts, with multiple beginnings, numerous failures, complex intermixtures and evolutionary dead ends.

Increasingly, it appears that modern humans did not develop directly from a single ancestral hominid but rather resulted from a pan-African evolutionary process in which numerous known and unknown subspecies of *Homo erectus* (the most successful hominid to date that survived some 1.5 million years, much longer than modern humans) mixed and remixed over hundreds of thousands of years. Various forms of *Homo erect*us, as well as species such as Neanderthals and Denisovans who emerged from them, spread out of Africa across Eurasia where they lived for at least 100,000 years. Modern humans, *Homo sapiens*, who first appeared in Africa around 300,000 years before the present, did not spread rapidly around the globe. For perhaps 250,000 years they were confined to Africa, and their dispersion took place not just once but multiple times with false starts and failures. As early as 50,000 years ago, *Homo sapiens* had arrived in Europe and begun to interbreed with Neanderthals, but this early tentative at establishing a presence north of the Mediterranean failed and this particular genetic line disappeared without a trace in later humans. It was not until some 10,000 years later that the direct ancestors of present-day humans began to appear outside of Africa, where they lived alongside (and occasionally mated with) other descendants of *Homo erectus*, including Neanderthal and Denisovan cousins, for roughly 7,000 years. Ultimately, these other subspecies disappeared, although the genetic record cannot tell whether they simply failed to thrive in a changing global climate or were exterminated by their *Homo sapiens* relatives, who went on to populate Eurasia, the Americas, Australia and finally, roughly 5,000 years ago, Micronesia and the Pacific Islands as far west as Hawaii.[2]

These 'big picture' studies covering tens of thousands of years are radically changing our understanding of our past and posing challenges to our understanding of what it means to be human now and in the future. At the same time, much more focused studies of the genetics of people who lived in the more recent past, that is, up to roughly 5,000 years before the present, are likewise changing how we understand more recent historical periods and thus how we understand historically recorded societies from which we draw our contemporary identities. However, while using the same tools of DNA extraction and sequencing, applying these to recent, very short periods and limited geographical areas require, as we will see in subsequent chapters, a radical refining of the analyses necessary to trace the minute but significant differences that separate not whole species but members of the same species whose communities diverged and remixed in the last few thousand, if not hundreds, of years.

While it is technically difficult to sequence DNA from bone fragments tens of thousands of years old, it is easy to separate

Neanderthals from *Homo sapiens* by their genetic profiles. It takes many different skills to distinguish among closely related individuals and communities that lived in intimate proximity at the same time. Studies that concentrate on short periods of a few hundred years and areas of a few thousand square kilometres require not only a refining of genetic tools but different strategies of sampling and an unprecedented level of collaboration among geneticists, historians and archaeologists.

Toward a genetic history of the Early Middle Ages

A particularly significant period in which genetic evidence is challenging conventional history is the period between the disappearance of the Roman Empire in western Eurasia and the emergence of modern European polities, that period between roughly 400 CE and 900 CE called Late Antiquity or the Early Middle Ages. The importance of this period for its deep political, social and cultural changes that would transform western Eurasia is in inverse proportion to the amount of available evidence, both written and archaeological, to help us understand the complex processes by which this transformation took place.

Vastly more written documents have survived from previous and of course subsequent periods, making these centuries of radical change particularly difficult to understand. From the Ancient Near East, today we have thousands of clay tablets that have been preserved and deciphered, providing an extraordinary view of daily life, society, religion, culture and politics in the so-called Fertile Crescent that today includes Iran, Iraq and the shores of the western Mediterranean. The Egyptian sands have preserved vast amounts of inscriptions as well as papyrus texts that illuminate 3,000 years of Egyptian history. From the Roman Empire, we have an extensive literature in Latin and Greek as well as abundant stone inscriptions and thousands of papyrus documents recovered from the Egyptian desert that provide a deep insight into the lives of the great and not so great. After our period, beginning in the eighth century, monastic, episcopal and ultimately civic archives began to preserve a whole spectrum of religious, literary, administrative and private documents that, by the Renaissance, numbered in the millions.

However, from that crucial period when the cultural, religious, political and social systems of Europe radically changed as the Roman Empire disappeared and, in its place, new polities with new forms of society and identity appeared across Europe, very few written documents or contemporary texts have survived. Likewise, inscriptions began to disappear in the fourth century and continued to be rare and laconic until around the year 1000.

Contrary to popular opinion, these centuries hardly constituted a 'dark age' of illiteracy and ignorance. Across the post-Roman world, urban and religious centres as well as government bureaucracies continued to produce a vast amount of administrative, fiscal and private types of documentation. The written word continued to be essential to the post-Roman world and, whether or not a specific individual could read or write, writing continued to play a major role in people's lives. Records of purchases and sales of land and movable property, rent rolls, wills, documents of enfranchisement and official administrative documents generated by regional centres and municipal governments continued to be generated by the thousands. Likewise, educated post-Romans continued to correspond by letter, to write histories and to record a myriad of ordinary as well as extraordinary events of daily life. However, almost all of this was written on papyrus, an abundant but fragile medium which, in humid, cold Europe, unlike the deserts of Egypt, is subject to decay and loss without exceptional care.[3] Thus, with few exceptions, this mass of documentation has disintegrated or disappeared across western and central Europe through the intervening centuries. Only when more durable parchment – first used for books and then, beginning in the seventh century, for official documents – became the normal writing material do we see a continuous written record that documents the lives of European men and women.

In those crucial regions beyond the Roman frontiers, among peoples termed barbarians by Romans and Greeks alike, writing was rarely used, confined to incised runic inscriptions on bone, wood or, more rarely, metal, and used primarily for religious or magical purposes. As these peoples moved into the Empire, either as mercenary armies with their families enlisted by the Empire or as uninvited conquerors, in some areas such a Gaul, Italy and the Iberian Peninsula, they incorporated Roman written tradition. In other areas, such as Britain, along the former Rhine and Danubian frontiers as well as in the Balkans, writing largely disappeared along with the Roman infrastructure that had preserved it.

As a result, historians seeking to understand the complex social, political and cultural changes that took place between the fourth and ninth centuries both within and without the Empire have had to rely on a very few written sources, all written by Roman or Greek authors who were often distant observers in time and place from these changes. These authors, trained in the long tradition of Greek and Roman ethnography which, with few exceptions, represented barbarian peoples as distinct, immutable entities, clearly distinguished by differentiations such as their fashions of dress, their weapons or their hairstyles, used inherited categories and topoi to describe their subjects. Moreover, in keeping with the classical tradition of historiography, these authors focused on the actions of kings, rulers and armies, to which they assigned ethnic labels. They showed little interest in the analysis of social structures or practices, nor the cultural values of these non-Roman populations and, when they did provide such analysis, they were often deeply influenced by the stereotypes they found in ancient literature.

These authors seldom indicated the sources of their information, and even when they did, those sources are often lost and scholars are unable to determine with certainty their quality.[4] To make matters even worse, even these texts are often transmitted in a fragmentary manner as excerpts in later histories, and have been subjected to editing and interpolations by successive generations of copyists whose interest in these texts was rarely simply to preserve an accurate record of the past.

Increasingly, then, historians have had to turn to other types of evidence to understand this period both within and without the former Roman Empire. Archaeology, and particularly funerary archaeology, has become an essential tool in this process. Since the later nineteenth century, across Europe the analysis of funerary remains, the organization of cemeteries, and the changes in burial customs have been key in coming to terms with the major transformations of the period. Archaeologists have developed detailed, geographically differentiated maps of the change from cremation to inhumation burials; they have analysed the transition from large urban sites to smaller communities and the appearance of rural cemeteries in which the dead were arranged in rows; they have charted the change in the orientation of burials in these row cemeteries. They have developed typologies of grave goods such as jewellery, weapons, tools and other artefacts buried with the dead, as well as the differing forms, depths and other characteristics of individual graves. They have used these multiple variables to create first relative and then absolute chronologies in order to date the appearance and spread of distinct burial traditions. Likewise, they have hypothesized population movements, migrations, various types of identities as well as religious and cultural change based on changes in this material culture.

Physical anthropologists, working closely with field archaeologists, analyse skeletal material to determine diet, health status and, tentatively, biological relationships among the dead by looking for genetically transmitted characteristics. Together, these scientists have used physical and material evidence to try to understand such phenomena as social organization, migration and cultural change.

Nevertheless, when scholars attempt to fit archaeological and anthropological material into a wider historical framework, much remains obscure. Do changes in material culture take place because of population movements or changes in fashion? Do material culture complexes – say the appearance of certain types of female ornamentation – indicate that those who were so buried shared a common political or ethnic identity? Does the disappearance of grave goods indicate conversion to Christianity? Does the organization of cemeteries represent the social organization of the society of the living? To what extent can the sparse written record be reconciled with the material without falling into a vicious cycle in which evidence is forced into a pre-existing model?

Not surprisingly, therefore, geneticists, with improved methodologies, are attempting to provide a new and powerful tool that can go beyond written texts and archaeological analyses to uncover the past. However, this is not the first time that something similar has been attempted, and then, as now, dangers abound if this new tool is misused. In order to avoid the errors of the past, we need to be aware of them even as we move into a new world of archeaogenetics.

Recognizing both the dangers of misuse as well as the possibilities of positive contributions of these new methods, this brief survey is intended to introduce readers to the challenges and the possibilities of integrating genomic data along with archaeological, historical and anthropological data in order to develop a deeper understanding of this crucial period. We must begin with the history of previous attempts to integrate biological, historical and archaeological data because we must be aware of the terrible consequences of the misuse of this data in the past as a warning for the future. In particular, we must be constantly aware of the danger of conflating genetic categories with cultural or ethnic categories. Since genomic analysis and population genetics are not typically part of the training that historians and many archaeologists receive, we must review basic genetics in order to understand the nature of genetic data, its possibilities for historical inquiry, but also its limits. Likewise, we will explain some of the basic analytic tools that geneticists use to analyse their data. Finally, we will review some of the most exciting results that have begun to emerge from this novel collaboration, with a particular focus on the European Research Council-sponsored project HistoGenes, that has combined historical, genetic, anthropological and archaeological data on a scale never before seen to understand the transformation of the Carpathian Basin, a region of enormous change, between the fourth and tenth centuries.

1

The Dangerous Legacy of Racialized History

The reasons that historians have largely ignored genomic data are, in part at least, understandable. One obvious reason is that for many significant historical questions, genetic data are simply useless: intellectual history, cultural history and much of political and economic history operate on very different types of data: primarily written texts that convey explicit meaning and intentionality. For historians interested in the thought lives of past generations, genetics holds little interest.

From the perspective of archaeologists, advances in physical anthropology, stable isotopic analysis and other microbiological technologies provide insight into the diet, health, physical activity and mobility of past generations. LIDAR (Light detection and ranging) as well as other techniques of non-invasive archaeology have created new possibilities of conducting site surveys and uncovering the past. Thus, over the past two centuries, the disciplines of archaeology and history have developed highly specialized methodologies for reconstructing the recent human past from osteological, material and written records. Practitioners of these disciplines have only occasionally looked to the developing field of ancient DNA research to supplement their analyses. Some are scornful of the suggestion that genomic data can replace written texts or material culture to understand the recent human past, an application dismissed by one archaeologist as 'a technique in search of applications'.[1]

However, there are other areas of history, such as social history, disease history, gender history, migration history and the like, that can profit from integrating genomic data into the textual, material and oral data that are the common tools of such historical research. Genomic data have the potential of making it possible for scholars to ask new questions and to open new lines of inquiry into the past. However, if recourse to ancient DNA solves some problems, its use to understand the recent human past raises new ones, and historians and many archaeologists have been reluctant if not overtly hostile to incorporating it into their research. Unfortunately, they have good reasons for their scepticism.

A dark past

The recent revolution in genetics is not the first time that scholars have attempted to combine archaeology, physical anthropology, history and biology to understand the human past. Humanists, looking at recent studies that apply biology to history, are instantly reminded of one of the darkest periods of historical studies. Chief among these, and particularly present in the concerns of humanistic historians confronted with genetic history, is the ghost of Gustaf Kossinna and his generation of archaeologists who, in the first quarter of the twentieth century, attempted in their own way to combine history, archaeology and biological evidence to understand human history.[2] Kossinna, along with contemporaries such as the Polish archaeologist, prime minister and later German collaborationist Leon Kozłowski in Poland,[3] and the Australian Gordon Childe in Scotland,[4] developed what is termed the *Siedlungsarchäologische Methode* as part of what in German was called *Rassenkunde*, the scientific study of human race.

These archaeologists were not the first to equate specific archaeological cultures and specific peoples, nor were they the first to assume that physiognomy could be used to infer character, intelligence and ethnic or racial origin. Rather, they were the inheritors of multiple scientific and pseudo-scientific movements that in the course of the later eighteenth and nineteenth centuries sought to classify and rank human diversity.

The first were the theories of such romantic philosophers as Johann Gottfried Herder (1774–1803) and Georg Wilhelm Friedrich Hegel (1770–1831), who argued that language, ancestry, identity and a 'Volksgeist' or 'folk spirit' defined and delineated peoples. This 'folk spirit' was unique to a particular people and remained unchanging across the centuries.[5] Although initially such ideas were not primarily political, during the tumultuous period of the French Revolution and especially of the Napoleonic Wars, they were quickly taken up, first in the German lands, but increasingly across Europe as a foundational element of romantic national awakening movements combining philology and history to argue for political autonomy.[6]

Simultaneously, authors with different agendas not only confirmed the differences among peoples or 'races', but classified them hierarchically. In the mid-eighteenth century, the Swedish biologist Carl Linnaeus (1707–78) proposed to classify humans according to four races: *Homo Europaeus*, *Homo Americanus*, *Homo Asiaticus* and *Homo Africanus*, each with its own skin colour, character and culture.[7] The British antiquarian John Pinkerton (1758–1826) developed a racial theory that argued that what he termed Goths or Scythians were the ancestors of most Europeans, including the Germans, Scandinavians, Greeks and Romans. His particular animus was directed at the Celts, who 'were so inferior a people, being to the Scythæ as a negro to a European, that, as all history shews, to see them, was to conquer them; and as they had no arts, or inventions, of their own, they of course received innumerable words from other tongues'.[8]

While Pinkerton's arguments, drawn from specious readings of classical, medieval and modern texts, some indeed forged by Pinkerton himself, were hardly mainstream, by the first half of the nineteenth century, comprehensive racial theories were increasingly entering serious intellectual debate. One of the most influential figures in this movement was Arthur de Gobineau (1816–22), a French diplomat and writer who, shaken by the events of the revolutions of 1848, authored an *Essai sur l'inégalité des races humaines*[9] in which he argued that humanity is divided into three races, white, black and yellow, each with its distinct characteristics. Even within the white race he found a hierarchy, with the Aryan race superior in intelligence, creativity and energy. In the course of the nineteenth century, these racial theories, buoyed by Darwin's theory of evolution, and working in harmony with European imperialism, developed into complex and at times competing classifications of different European populations and hierarchies.[10]

At the same time that nationalist movements were emphasizing the distinction of peoples based on culture, language and history and that social scientists were classifying and ranking racial groups, practitioners of the nascent field of physical anthropology were seeking to categorize populations based on physical measurements, primary on cranial shapes.[11] The founders of this pseudo-science, Franz Joseph Gall (1758–1828) and his research partner and later rival Johan Spurzheim (1776–1832) believed that the various functions of the brain determined an individual's fundamental character and abilities, and that these sections of the brain were reflected in the size, shape and characteristics of the skull. In the course of the nineteenth century, these theories were widely adopted not only by anatomists and anthropologists such as Paul Pierre Broca (1824–80), the founder of French physical anthropology, but also criminologists such as Cesare Lombroso (1835–1909), who developed a theory of classification of 'criminal types' based on skull measurements. A key measurement used to classify populations was the cephalic index, which characterized individuals as dolichocephalic (long-headed), mesaticephalic (moderate-headed) or brachycephalic (short-headed), categories used both to map populations and to establish racial hierarchies. Individual anthropologists, learned societies and museums amassed great collections of skulls, many still preserved in museums and anthropological institutes, in order to classify humanity.[12]

Across Europe and in the United States, nationalism, colonialism, racialism, Darwinism and physical anthropology combined into what would become eugenics and scientific racism, widely accepted by societies, governments and learned societies.[13]

Drawing on such conceptions, Gustav Kossinna, like many archaeologists, philologists and historians of his era, understood European peoples as homogeneous political, linguistic, cultural and biological units that were assumed to have had a discrete Original Homeland, identifiable through archaeology.

A map drawn up by the philologist Johansson, of the putative original homelands of the Indo-Europeans, and reproduced by Kossinna, for example, shows geographically bounded, discrete cultural areas and arrows suggesting migratory paths of these peoples. Kossinna had no problem with these assumptions but he believed that such a map, drawn exclusively on linguistic evidence, was inadequate. Rather, he was convinced that wanderings could be traced by combining antique written sources, Indo-European philology, and archaeological finds from these homelands across Europe. Kossinna moreover firmly believed that the coincidence of culture and people was a universal.

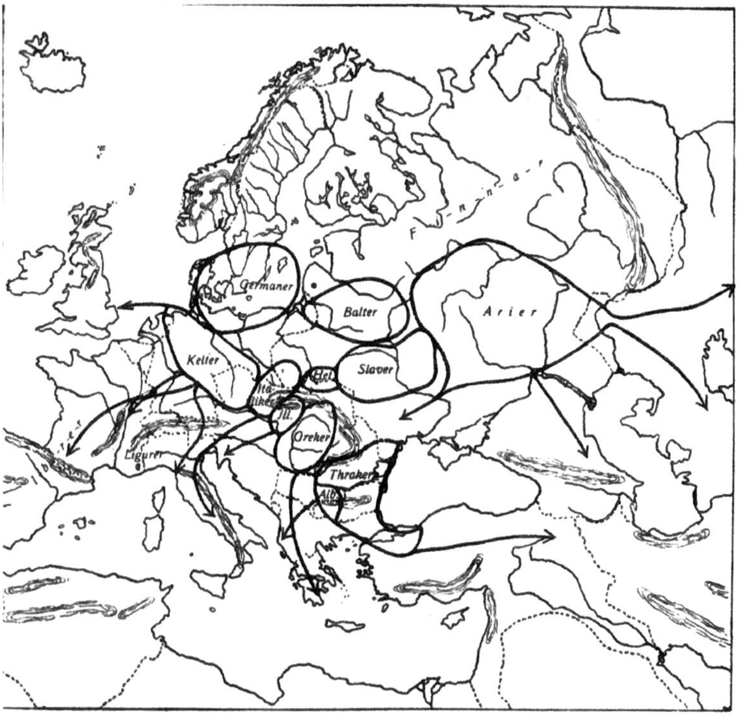

Abb. 84. Ursitze der indogermanischen Völker (nach K. F. Johansson).

FIGURE 1 *Putative homelands of Germanic peoples. Kossinna,* Ursprung und Verbreitung der Germanen, *fig. 84, 71.*

Although some archaeologists continue to apply a modified version of the *Siedlungsarchäologische Methode*, identifying particular objects or burial practices as ‘Frankish’, ‘Hunnic’, ‘Lombard’ and so on, Kossinna is today regularly repudiated and criticized, both for his attempts to identify ancient *Völker* by combining archaeological, linguistic, biological and textual evidence, and even more for his ready acceptance of a hierarchy within the peoples of Europe.[14] His practice of identifying cultural areas by mapping distinct types of pottery and their distribution, which he attributed to migrations, is well known, as is his practice of identifying some of these pottery types with population expansion and migration. Of course, he went even further, identifying specific forms of material culture with distinct linguistic groups and sub-groups, particularly with Indo-Europeans and, at a finer level, east Germanic speakers, as in the following map of the supposed homelands of Burgundians and Vandals (Figure 2).

Note that in the putative settlement area Kossinna presents as the primitive homeland of the east Germanics, the thin line indicates the boundary between the Burgundians (in the north) and the Vandals (in the south and east). His 'evidence' for the division of these populations relies on material culture differences.

However, Kossinna sought to add an additional dimension to the study of material culture and linguistic cultures: the biological. Drawing on the methods of phrenology, he used skull shapes to categorize the populations that he sought to understand. For example, studying what he considered an expansion of Indo-

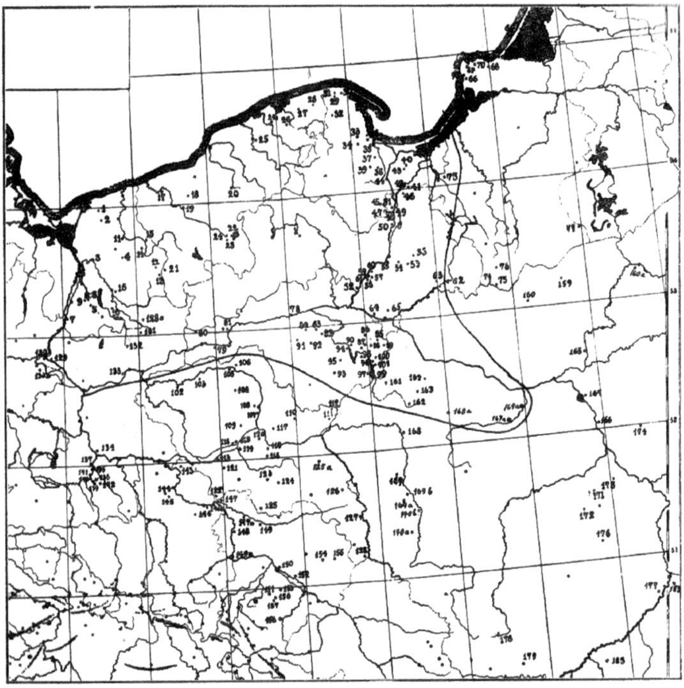

Abb. 24. **Siedelungen der Ostgermanen während des 1. Jahrhunderts vor Chr. (nach Kostrzewski).**
Die dickere Linie bezeichnet die Grenze des burgundisch-rugischen Gebiets (im Norden) und des wandalischen Gebiets (im Süden und Osten).

FIGURE 2 *Putative settlement areas of east-Germanics in the first century* BCE. *Kossinna,* Ursprung und Verbreitung der Germanen, *fig. 24.*

European population in north-west Germany, he combined a type of pottery that he termed 'Rössener' after the site of Rössen an der Saale, with specific skull types.

Kossinna characterizes the skull, shown in Figure 4, as 'Steep forehead and tapered back, typical of the great majority of skulls at

Abb. 185. 1/4 Rössen, Kr. Merseburg.

FIGURE 3 *Rössen pot from the area of Merseburg. Kossinna,* Ursprung und Verbreitung der Germanen, *fig. 184, 165.*

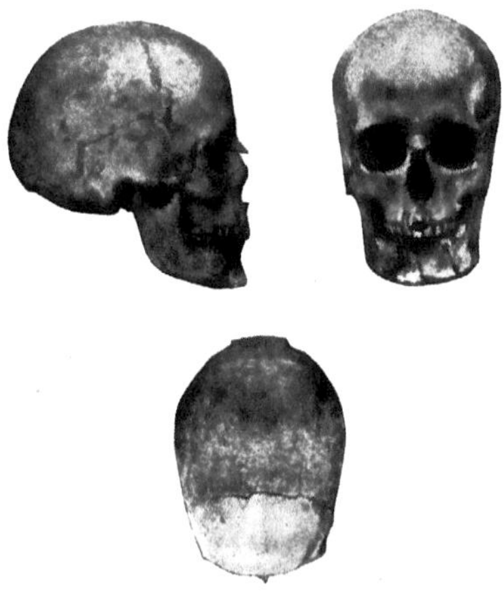

Abb. 192 a–c. Rössen, Kr. Merseburg.
Schädel 3608, Abart A (nach Schliz).

FIGURE 4 *Rössen, area of Merseburg, Skull 3608. Kossinna,* Ursprung und Verbreitung der Germanen, *fig. 182, 167.*

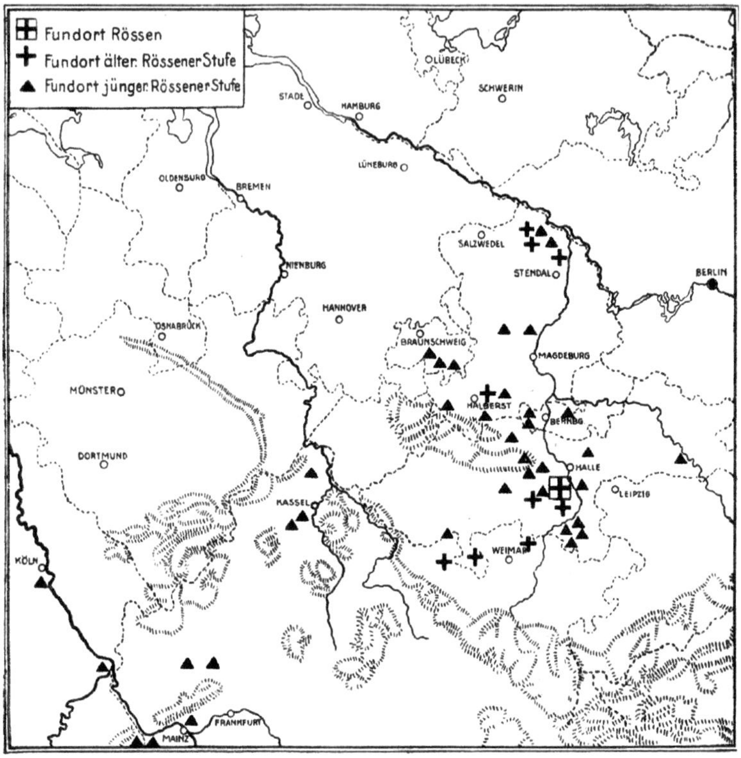

Abb. 184. Verbreitung der Rössener Kulturstufe.

FIGURE 5 *The expansion of Rössner culture. Kossinna,* Ursprung und Verbreitung der Germanen, *fig. 184, 164.*

Rössen.'[15] From the distribution of this pottery type and these skull forms, he then constructed a map of the expansion of the 'Rössener Culture' area.

Nor did Kossinna stop here. He sought, across Europe, evidence in the skull forms of his contemporary Europeans of the expansion of the Germanic peoples into the Roman Empire. For example, this individual from the province of Vicenza, Italy (Figure 6), was supposed to demonstrate the influence of the Langobard invasion into Italy in the sixth century or the expansion of Germans into north-eastern Italy in the late Middle Ages.

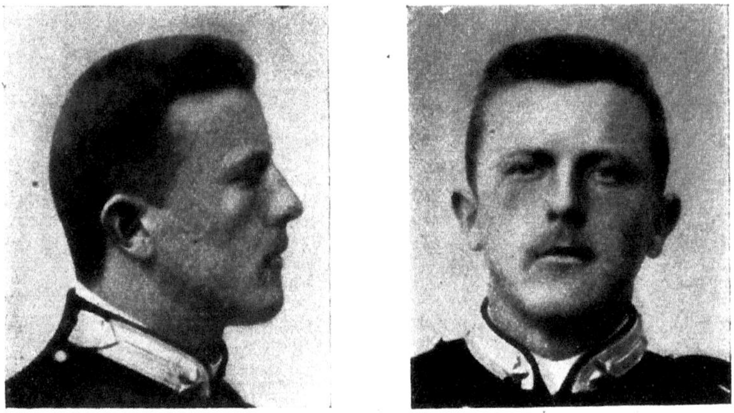

Abb. 130 a, b. Kurzkopf 85,2; blond, germanisches Gesicht.
Sette Comuni, Prov. Vicenza (nach Ripley).

FIGURE 6 *Putative Germanic skull type from Italy. Kossinna,* Ursprung und Verbreitung der Germanen, *fig. 130a, 119.*

For Kossinna, there was a clear hierarchy among the peoples of Europe, a hierarchy that saw of course the Germanic at the apex (although he himself was of Mazury ancestry, a region today in Poland). His combination of the methodologies of archaeology, linguistics and physical anthropology allowed an understanding of Europe's population both in the past and the present:

> The physical remains of the indigenous people of our country, which we have gotten to know here as precisely as the current state of our science allows, teach which ancestors we descend from and which we do not. But racial science achieves even greater insofar as it not only reveals the physical, but also the mental and spiritual peculiarities of today's breeds, that is, the meaningful differences of the races in this direction.[16]

Kossinna died in 1931. The uses to which his combined methodology of archaeology, history, linguistics and biology were put during the decade and a half following his death by German ideologues is too well known to require comment. In addition, certainly, in the past generation, careful historical scholarship has fundamentally rejected both Kossinna's methodologies and the Herderan image of 'Avalanche of peoples' it was used to support.[17]

The revisionist history of early medieval population movement

This revisionist enterprise has thus far been carried on first through the analysis of the sparse documentary evidence of late antique and early medieval texts, texts that are constantly being reinterpreted by the application of insights developed from comparative history, sociology and cultural anthropology. For global historians, population movements in the Early Middle Ages have also been analysed through comparative studies of migration and population changes diachronically and across Eurasia.[18] The term migration itself has come under scrutiny, since the very term can carry so many different meanings both across disciplines and in popular usage. For population geneticists, migration is synonymous with 'gene flow' and is but one explanation among others to explain changes in allele frequencies in populations. Historians and sociologists use the term when describing both long distance movements of individuals, families, or groups between regions and short distance movements from village to village or from the countryside to the city. It has been used to describe such long term processes as the gradual expansion of agriculturalists from the Near East into Europe and that took over a millennium and may have involved individuals moving only a few kilometres in a generation, a process perhaps better termed diffusion. Migration can be voluntary or forced, permanent, or circular, seasonal, or temporary. Individual or group migration can result in full or partial fusion of the newly arrived individuals into the existing population or even, in rare circumstances, population replacement. Moreover, comparative studies suggest that Europe has always known population movements, and the most important of these have been processes of demic diffusion, chain migration or the movement of specialized categories such as soldiers or miners, not whole communities. The nineteenth-century image of barbarian migrations as movements of whole populations sharing the same language, culture, political and social systems, and presumably ancestry across

Europe, while still represented in popular maps, textbooks, and popular discourse, is hopelessly out of date.

Likewise, new generations of archaeologists have introduced fundamentally new ways of interpreting material culture in terms of local communities, social hierarchies, exchange and life cycles rather than reducing observed patterns to issues of race or ethnicity. Changes in patterns of material culture have offered explanations rooted in cultural transfer rather than migration and conquest.[19]

The results of this revisionist approach as applied to the so-called Migration Period are significant if still controversial. The discrete, homogeneous peoples of the Romantic Era are increasingly understood as heterogeneous, *ad hoc* constellations created under specific historical circumstances. Often the impetus for the ethnogenesis of a new people has been deemed to be the Roman world itself, which both actively and passively contributed to the formation of new peoples. Roman mercantile penetration beyond the *limes* into barbarian territory, in search of raw materials, amber and slaves, destabilized the equilibrium of small scale, traditional societies of farmers and herders. More dramatically, Roman state policy sought to shore up chieftains who might support Roman interests, restrain raiding into the Empire and provide auxiliary troops to the Roman army when needed. The result, so the theory goes, was the emergence of more hierarchical, larger-scale polities on the periphery of the Empire, polities so deeply imbricated with the Empire itself, that the Austrian historian Herwig Wolfram would write about 'The Roman Empire and *its* Germanic Peoples'.[20] Likewise, in reaction to pressure from Rome and its barbarians, other groups could coalesce into new, anti-Roman polities such as the Marcomanni or the Alemanni, drawing together otherwise disparate groups who shared a need for protection or a desire for plunder. To the extent that these 'peoples' were constituted under historical circumstances, it logically follows that they could also disappear, subsumed into new constellations, again changing their identities with changing circumstances.

Likewise, the processes that led to the presence of non-Roman groups within the Empire are being understood, not in terms of a restless search for a new homeland or mass movements of whole peoples, but rather discrete incursions that took place in the context of the civil wars that wracked the western half of the Empire in its last centuries. Perhaps the most succinct statement of this new understanding is that of Guy Halsall, who argues powerfully that stresses in the Empire from around 400 'created political vacuums at local and regional levels in the western Empire, into which non-Roman political, social and military units were drawn'. He concludes that 'The "barbarian migrations" were, therefore, the product of the "end of the Roman Empire," and not vice versa.'[21]

However, much remains unclear about European population change at the end of the Roman period. We know that at various times in history, short-term, dramatic migrations have indeed taken place. At the end of the Second World War, some ten million people in eastern Europe fled persecution and starvation into the west, and we are experiencing one at present, as people flee war, starvation and poverty in the eastern and southern Mediterranean and Africa into western Europe. Likewise, demic expansions have certainly taken place, although whether these resulted in the replacement of the indigenous population or its gradual absorption depends on time and place. Moreover, while it may well be that many early medieval peoples were *ad hoc* constellations of various groups, some indeed seem to have had a cohesion and self-identity that could withstand conquest, subordination and temporary absorption by conquerors over centuries.

Thus, as historians, we are faced with the need to ask, of the various types of population changes that have been seen in world history which took place in western Eurasia between the fourth and ninth centuries, was this 'business as usual' or a period of intensification? Should we not distinguish among a variety of modalities during these centuries, from elite takeovers by small barbarian military units drawn into Roman civil wars to more massive invasions of men, women and children, to chain migrations that took place over generations, to broad demic expansions of the Franks or especially the Slavs? One model certainly does not fit all: there is no reason that the transformation of Britain into Anglo-Saxon kingdoms in the fifth century should be the same process that saw the emergence of the Frankish kingdoms in the fifth century or of the Langobard kingdom of Italy in the sixth. Nor need one assume that the internal composition of the Saxons, Franks, Alemanni, Heruli or Langobards followed the same patterns. Likewise, to assume that the role of Steppe warriors in Europe, be they the Huns, Avars or Magyars, was always the same.

So how do we go beyond the laconic written evidence and the ambiguous archaeological evidence to elucidate these processes?

How can we understand the internal social and cultural composition of the various actors, their numbers, their movements and, ultimately, their effects on the European population? Increasingly, geneticists are attempting to provide new data both to answer old questions and to allow us to ask new questions about the gendered nature of early medieval societies, the place of children in them, the extent to which endogamy was practised by different cultural and political groups and the size and demographic impact of newly arrived populations within the Roman Empire.

Neo-Kossinnan genomics

Frankly, this is dangerous. Let us remember what Kossinna and his contemporaries were doing with their measurements of skulls. Not having direct access to genetic data (while DNA has been known since 1869, its function and role were not recognized until after Kossinna's death),[22] Kossinna was in effect looking at a phenotype, skull morphology, as a stand-in for genotype, much as the Italian geneticist Luigi Luca Cavalli-Sforza[23] in the 1960s began to use blood types of living people to attempt to reconstruct ancient population structures. Kossinna then generalized from what he considered 'typical' skull types by region to categorize the populations of these regions, that he then equated with a particular material culture and, drawing on the work of Indo-European philologists, with a linguistic culture. Finally, he tracked the movement of these composites across Europe by observing incidences of both material culture changes and the appearance of a percentage of his skull types. The resemblance of Kossinna's methodology and that of some contemporary genetic history approaches is striking.

Even into the twenty-first century, some geneticists begin with the same premises. For example, as the Cambridge archaeologist Susanne Hakenbeck has pointed out, a number of recent studies attempting to determine the origins of the Indo-Europeans begin with the archaeological complexes that would be entirely familiar to Kossinna, such as the 'corded ware people' or the 'bell beaker people'.[24] The maps developed by geneticists strongly resembled those already produced by Kossinna. In seeking their biological evidence for these peoples, they do not look to skull morphology, but rather genome sequences of samples taken from the areas included in the archaeologically generated regions. In one study, this meant a sample size of 101 individuals from across Eurasia who lived between 3000 and 1000 BCE.[25] We can see that the same procedure is used to overlay cultures derived from pottery types with genomic data (see Figure 7).

Another study focused on sixty-nine Europeans who lived between 6000 and 1000 BCE and uses such phrases as 'Late Neolithic Corded Ware people from Germany traced 75 per cent of their ancestry to the Yamnaya,' thus identifying a cultural practice, again a type of pottery, with a 'people' who had a specific genetic signal.[26]

A superficial reading of these two studies could easily give the impression that some of their approaches and interpretations are quite similar to those of Kossinna and his contemporaries. Some of the early attempts in the still very young discipline of historical genetic research were indeed influenced by the tendency of older archaeological research to assign material culture complexes to specific peoples or ethnic groups. Such essentialization from both the humanities and the natural sciences is certainly dangerous. However, more critical views are now well established in both disciplines, archaeology and historical genetic research. The idea that the 'Corded Ware people' or 'Yamnaya culture' represent clearly defined ethnic groups or peoples has been abandoned in modern archaeology. 'Pots are not peoples' is now a generally accepted slogan, although the tendency to underestimate the role of migration in cultural change is, as we shall see in Chapter 4, increasingly in need of modification.[27] And the leading representatives of historical genetic research are well aware of the dangers of misuse of their data and point out in their genetic analyses that their samples do not have a homogeneous genetic profile, but are the result of complex admixtures.[28] For example, even if genetic diversity is recognized, it is of little help if it is linked to older archaeological work in which the Corded Ware culture or the Yamnaya culture represent distinct or definable cultural groups. The problem becomes even more acute when the names of ethnic groups or peoples known from written sources, such as the Saxons, Huns or Lombards, are used to classify archaeological or genetic patterns, since these names are essentially subjective cultural projections and not objective descriptions of archaeological or genetic complexes.

The result, no less than in the day of Kossinna, is that such studies tend toward a simplified, essentializing of past societies.

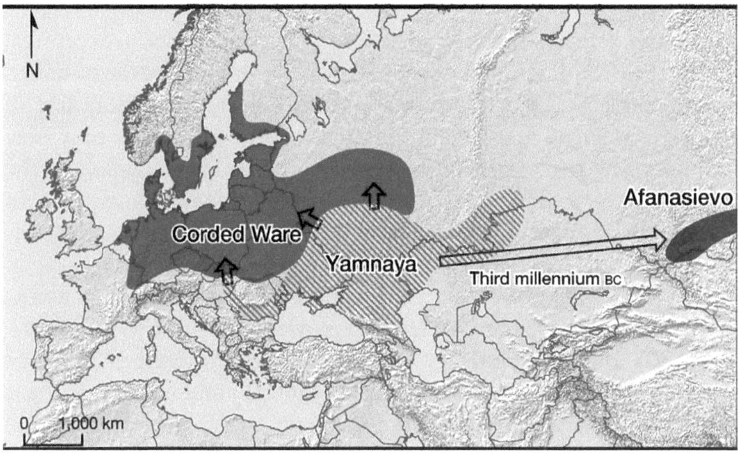

FIGURE 7 *Attempt to show areas of cultures/peoples based on genetics. M. E. Allentoft et al., 'Population genomics of Bronze Age Eurasia',* Nature *522 (2015), fig. 1, 168, https://doi.org/10.1038/nature14507. Reproduced by permission of Springer Nature.*

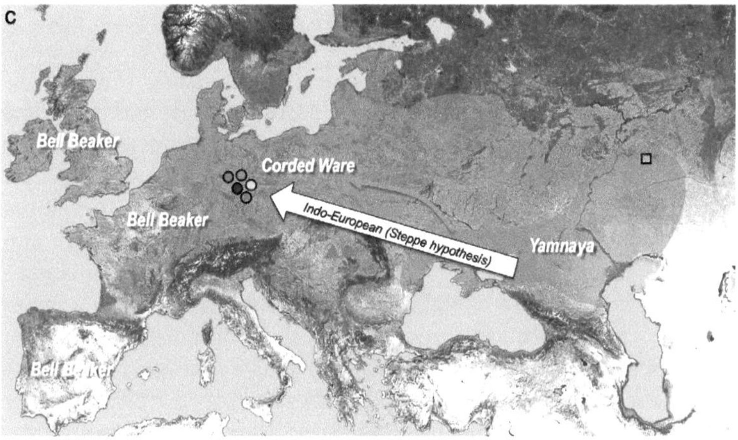

FIGURE 8 *Archaeological cultures as populations. W. Haak et al., 'Massive migration from the Steppe was a source for Indo-European languages in Europe',* Nature *522 (2015): 207–11, extended data fig 4, https://doi.org/10.1038/nature14317. Reproduced by permission of Springer Nature.*

Small wonder then that historians of the European past are sceptical about the introduction of genetic data into the study of the so-called Migration Period. Rather than an advance in our understanding of the past through new methodologies, they see a risk that new technologies will reaffirm old ideologies. And certainly, in the popular press and the blogosphere precisely this is taking place. In the current climate of renascent ethnic nationalism and racism, this return to the past poses a grave danger to society.[29]

This is where the difficulty of developing critical approaches across disciplinary boundaries becomes particularly clear: geneticists, historians and archaeologists each have their own understanding of terms such as population, people, ethnicity and group in their disciplines. Worse, they sometimes adopt outdated concepts from other disciplines, such as the meaning of culture or ethnicity, without understanding the theoretical discussions around these terms. However, the differences between these differentiated terms are often lost in joint publications – a problem that is exacerbated not least by the much more compact form of scientific publications. The reduced presentation of the results is therefore often received very critically by archaeologists and historians. The short and sometimes abbreviated presentation of the research, which they are less used to, gives them little opportunity to recognize the critical interdisciplinary work behind it.

Many therefore fear that such studies are still in Kossinna's shadow and continue the simplistic and essentializing views of the past that were so influential in older archaeology and historical research. Instead of improving our understanding of the past through new methods, they see the risk that new technologies will reinforce old ideologies. It is all the more important that scientists develop a common language and perspective for these questions, which can only be answered jointly by natural scientists and humanities scholars, in which we can also communicate our results to a wider public. The prerequisite for this is the continuation or even intensification of the dialogue and debate across disciplinary boundaries, as is being pursued and further developed in an exemplary manner by the work and projects at the Max Planck Institute for Human History and the work of Jörg Feuchter and Elsbeth Bösl.[30]

How can the new genomic analyses avoid the errors of the last century while actually contributing in a meaningful way to a deeper understanding of Eurasian history? This is the challenge that we will take up in the remaining chapters.

2

Genetic Data as Historical Data

Genetic data do not lie. But then, no data, whether written, oral or material, lie, simply because data as such do not speak. No written text 'speaks for itself'. No artefacts proclaim their meaning. Oral history is the end result of the creative process of human memory that is constantly adjusting, restructuring and revising the past. Every type of data requires interpretation, and it is in the interpretation that error, misjudgement or outright lying occurs. If we mistake a forgery for a genuine document; a literary fiction for an historical account; misinterpret the function of a tool or project meaning onto a potsherd; or fail to understand how an oral tradition came to be constructed and performed, we, not these sources, are in error. Historians and archaeologists are long familiar with these challenges. Thus, as we expand the scope of what we can consider historical evidence, we must develop equally precise methods for understanding the nature and limitations of new forms of evidence and how we can appropriately use them to understand the past.

At the beginning of the twentieth century, French scientific history began with conviction, 'l'histoire se fait avec des textes' or, in the reformulation by Charles-Victor Langlois and Charles Seignobos, 'L'histoire se fait avec des documents.'[1] Although too often dismissed as the battle cry of positivism, the main intention of such a declaration was to insist that serious history had to be based not on ideology, rhetoric, wishful thinking or self-serving memoires by great men and women, but rather on the careful study and exploitation of primary sources, principally archival, that put the historian in direct contact with the traces of the past. Nevertheless, subsequent generations of historians have demonstrated conclusively, in the words of Georges Duby, that 'l'histoire ne se fait pas qu'avec des textes'. First scholars and scientists investigating a vast spectrum of material artefacts, including not only data recovered from archaeology but also from isotopic analysis, geography, palaeobotany, soil science, climatology and other disciplines, have provided evidence about human societies and their differential changes over time that would remain entirely unknown if history were to limit itself to the written record. More recently, drawing on ethnographic and personal field experience, historians, first in Africa but now throughout the world, have been able to use oral traditions, once dismissed as hopelessly unreliable, to uncover part of the deep past of 'people without history', in the sense of people without the privileged access to the written word.[2] The result has been that history, the study of differential change in human society over time, is no longer limited to those societies that in the past 5,000 years produced written records but extends both vertically into the deep past of the human race and horizontally to include societies that did not employ the technology of writing. Today, the only way to accept the old dictum is to redefine 'text' as trace, that is, any and every bit of data that carries a trace of human thought or action in the past. Documents, objects, words: all must be considered. However, none of these traces speaks for itself: each has had to be 'tamed'; that is, practitioners of textual history, archaeology and oral history have had to develop careful methodologies so that we can understand what these traces are, according to what cultural and normative systems they were generated, and by what means they can be employed to understand the past.

The history of history is replete with negative examples of the misunderstanding, misappropriation and misuse of written sources. These range from simply mistaking forged documents for genuine to assuming authors accurately reported what they had seen or heard, when in fact they were guessing or projecting opinion as fact. Too often texts that were prescriptive, be they legal documents, edicts or religious proclamations, have been misunderstood as descriptive, accurately portraying the thoughts, deeds and aspirations of past actors. Historians who study serial records such as economic data, census reports or masses of legal records must first understand in detail how such records were compiled, what they contain and what they omit, and then they must find the right statistical methods to analyse them. Failing to do so leads to fundamental distortions in the reconstruction of the past. And of course, too often historians, trapped in their own unconscious ideologies and suppositions, project these onto their written sources, in effect not so much finding meaning in the textual record as imposing it.

The exploitation of material culture evidence into social, cultural and political history has been equally fraught, with scholars in disciplines such as archaeology, geology, palaeobotany or dendrochronology over-interpreting or simply misinterpreting their evidence. Again, such errors reach across a wide spectrum, from simply misdating or misidentifying material evidence from the past to over-interpretations based on a failure to recognize what material culture can and especially what it cannot tell about past societies.

Oral history, too, remains a complex and disputed terrain – human memory is extraordinarily creative and protean, with different societies having not only different systems within which to remember and recite the past but different categories of what telling the past might mean. In many societies, such as western Europe, oral traditions do not reach back much beyond a century, and these traditions are constantly inflected by the subsequent experiences of those doing the remembering. Thus, historians who rely on the memory of eyewitnesses often fail to recognize how much these memories have transformed the past that they purport to record. In other societies, more formal memory systems preserve information about ancestry, major individuals and important events. However, these too are not immune from transformation and especially selectivity: Collective memory is qualitatively different from written records, and historians who fail to recognize the differences risk significant distortion of the past.

Thus, much bad history has been written based on texts, on material objects and on oral traditions. Likewise, much bad history has resulted from inept attempts to integrate written, material and oral traces into a coherent whole by historians who failed to recognize the possibilities but also the limitations of interpretation of these different types of sources. No one trace provides a privileged access to the past and no one methodological or epistemological approach has proven adequate to exploit sufficiently all of the issues that arise when these qualitatively different sources are combined. We are agreed that we cannot exclude textual, material or oral sources in our attempt to understand the past. Nevertheless, we continue to debate just how this combined history is to be done.

Genetic data as historical evidence

The same dilemma faces, and must face, those scholars attempting to come to terms with the fourth trace – the vast amount of genetic data that every living being carries in its DNA. Every chromosome contains within it the sum of generations that produced it; all of the casual affairs, marriages, rapes and couplings of millennia, lumped by geneticists into the anodyne term 'gene flow'. In their Y chromosome, men carry the biological heritage of all of their fathers, while mitochondrial DNA connects men and women directly to all of their mothers. Nuclear DNA contains the complex record not only of the material and paternal lines but also traces of one's ancestry to the first humans and beyond. Nor is human DNA the only genetic data for human history: the genetic history of domesticated plants and animals, even the vermin and bacteria that inhabit the human body, carry with them the evidence of human migration, interaction and transformation. No less than texts, than material culture, than oral tradition, genetic data, the fourth trace, must be considered in understanding the long past of human societies. The problem, of course, is how to do this.

Until very recently, genetic history has been mostly focused on the study of very broad, ancient issues of human history and very narrow, recent ones. The time depth of the former is extreme, making the currently popular 'deep history' that starts about ten KYA (thousand years ago) seem like journalism. The genetic split that separated humans from our closest relatives took place some six to nine MYA (million years ago), with the first members of the genus *Homo* appearing approximately 2.4 MYA. The most significant contribution of genetic history to the study of early humanity has been in the long-disputed issue of the diversification and peopling of the globe.[3] Fossil evidence is necessarily incomplete and inconclusive for determining whether modern humans emerged fairly recently from a single species of hominid or if *Homo sapiens* are the result of developments of various hominid species at multiple locations that ultimately, through migrations and gene-flow, allowed them to share both cultural and genetic characteristics. While virtually every aspect of early hominid development continues to be debated, including the multiregional vs single-origin models, the evidence from complete mtDNA sequences, Y chromosome data and other genetic evidence all suggest that the ancestors of all modern humans originated in Africa around 200–300 KYA, and most of the 'action' in early human genetics is concerned with understanding the extraordinarily complex process by which African populations eventually populated the world, a process that seems to have started only fifty KYA.

More recently, ancient DNA analysis has brought clarification to the complex process by which the modern population of Europe emerged from three ancestral populations: west European Hunter-Gatherers, so-called Yamnaya Steppe populations, and Early European Farmers.[4]

At the other end of the spectrum, historians and biographers have had considerable success adopting the tools and techniques of forensic genetics to answer questions of recent kinship and descent. In North America, the most famous case is that of Sally Hemings, the slave of Thomas Jefferson.[5] Claims that Hemings had been Jefferson's concubine and had born him as many as six children began during his lifetime, but no corroborating evidence could be gathered until 1998, when a team of geneticists tested Y-chromosomal DNA samples from male-line descendants of Jefferson's uncle John Carr, the father of his cousins who had been suggested as possible alternative fathers, and descendants of two of Hemings's children, Thomas C. Woodson, Sally Hemings's first son, and Eston Hemings, her last. The results were very clear: there was no genetic link between the descendants of Thomas C. Woodson and Jefferson, nor was there any link between the descendants of John Carr and Eston Hemings. However, an individual with the same Y chromosome as Thomas Jefferson fathered Eston Hemings. Although there were twenty-five male Jeffersons alive at the time that Sally Hemings bore Eston, the most obvious and widely accepted conclusion is that Thomas Jefferson was the father of Eston, and probably of other Hemings children.

In Britain, the most widely followed use of aDNA was the identification of skeletal remains, found in a Leicester car park, with King Richard III (1452–85).[6] Richard had been buried in the church of the Grey Friars after his death at the Battle of Bosworth. In 2012, an excavation found a skeleton on the site of the long-vanished church whose pre- and post-mortem wounds corresponded to accounts of Richard's death and the subsequent mistreatment of his body. Although Richard had no descendants, scientists found a perfect mitochondrial DNA match between that of the skeleton and a living relative, the descendant of Richard's sister, Anne of York. Whole genome sequencing allowed the scientific team to determine the eye and hair colour of the individual, which corresponded to known portraits of the king. Ultimately, both the physical anthropological analyses, including age, sex and the presence of scoliosis and wounds as well as the genetic data allowed the team to conclude that the remains were indeed those of the king, and they were reburied in the Leicester Cathedral on 26 March 2015.

Most historians, however, are not primarily concerned with the sex lives of individual historical figures or the identification of the remains of long-dead kings. Historians tend to deal with mid-range issues, largely within five KYA and most with much more recent history. Moreover, while historical biographers legitimately want to understand the private lives of individuals, most historians deal with broader societal phenomena. Other than proving that the written sources concerning Richard's death were accurate and that, while suffering from scoliosis he was hardly the hunchback of Shakespeare's play, the detective work conducted by the genetics team at Leicester added nothing to our understanding of Richard and his reign, although parallel isotopic studies demonstrated where he had spent his youth. The challenge is to determine whether genetics can be applied to broader and more significant historical questions.

In order to answer this question, historians must, without becoming geneticists themselves, understand the basics of genetics, particularly since the field has rapidly changed since most of us studied genetics as undergraduates. It is essential to understand what genetic research can and cannot accomplish and to comprehend how geneticists go about their investigations.

What historians need to remember (or to learn) about genetics

When Luigi Luca Cavalli-Sforza began his pioneering work on human genetics and history, the primary genetic markers that he could trace were blood types.[7] Today genetic research has progressed, and continues to progress, at an extraordinary rate. Well into the twenty-first century, scholars and scientists who sought to use genomic data to understand history had what today are seen as woefully inadequate tools. As we saw above, geneticists long had to work backwards from modern datasets in order to identify patterns that might be explained by population changes centuries before. The study of ancient DNA only began in 1984, when Russell Higuchi, Barbara Bowman, Mary Freiberger, Oliver A. Ryder and Allan C. Wilson were able to sequence fragments of the mitochondrial DNA of an extinct quagga from a nineteenth-century museum specimen.[8] Since then, the possibilities of capturing, sequencing and analysing ancient DNA have expanded at an exponential rate. From this early success in sequencing 229 nucleotide pairs, it is possible to sequence the whole genome, which consists of roughly 3.2 billion base pairs. Today, it is possible to sequence the whole genome of individuals who lived hundreds and even thousands of years ago. We have learned what portions of the anatomy preserve the highest amount of DNA, and how to avoid the challenges of contamination and post-mortem degradation. Moreover, the costs of sequencing have dropped exponentially. In 2001, the cost of sequencing the first whole human genome was somewhere between $300 million and $1 billion, depending on what costs of the Human Genome Project are included. By 2011 the cost had dropped to roughly $10,000. Today, it is possible to sequence an entire genome for under $400. It is difficult even for geneticists to keep pace with the speed of new developments, and yet historians and archaeologists who hope to understand the possibilities and limitations of genetics for understanding the human past need at least a basic understanding of contemporary genetics in order to be able to read, understand and evaluate the research of geneticists. We begin therefore with a basic review of what we learned, or should have learned, about DNA.

Deoxyribonucleic acid (DNA), the basic material of virtually all living organisms, is a large molecule composed of repeating structural subunits or nucleotides that vary in different portions known as bases. The sequences of these four bases, adenine (A), guanine (G), cytosine (C) and thymine (T), carry the genetic information of all living things. These nucleotides are joined together on a sugar-phosphate backbone into long strands and these strands normally exist in cells as doubles spiralled around each other in a double helix. The bases on one strand pair with the bases of the other, with base pairing conforming strictly to the pattern that A and T pair only with each other just as do C and G. The lengths of double-stranded DNA molecules are described in units of base-pairs (BP) and for longer molecules in megabase-pairs (Mb). The human genome (that is, the entirety of material carrying hereditary information) is estimated at between 2,693 and 2,907 Mb. However, much of the human genome has no known function: it is estimated that only some 32,000 segments, termed genes, either contain instructions or function in their own right. These very large genomes are divided into forty-six separate molecules paired into twenty-three chromosomes.

With the exception of certain social insects, all animals have two copies of their genome in every cell (one copy from each parent); that is, they are diploid. Somatic cells (all those cells that make up part of a living organism except the reproductive cells) replicate via a form of cell division called mitosis. During this process each chromosome replicates, producing two identical sister chromatids for each chromosome, temporarily doubling the DNA content before the cell divides. The resulting sister chromatids then move to opposite poles of the cell and the nuclear envelope then reforms around each, resulting in two diploid cells identical to the parent cell in terms of chromosomal content.

In contrast, those cells that are part of the reproductive process, called germ cells, and progenitors for gametes (for example sperm and eggs) undergo a cell division process called meiosis that produces chromosomes that are genetically different from the parental ones. Initially the pairs of homologous chromosomes replicate and align and the cell divides into two much as in mitosis, but then the cells re-divide so the four resulting gamete cells contain only one copy of each chromosome (i.e., they result in haploid gametes). However, as importantly, during the initial process of meiosis when homologous chromosomes align, they exchange segments through a process called genetic recombination: no genetic information is lost, but the result of this recombination or crossing over is that the chromosomes in egg or sperm can be genetically different to the original parental copies, such that they are a mosaic of the chromosomes inherited from each parent. The molecular similarities and differences between homologous DNA sequences or alleles make it possible to observe inheritance of specific segments of DNA from parent to child. Moreover, counting the number of recombination events allows an estimation of genetic distance between markers, making possible genetic mapping. Recombination rates differ between the sexes and differ at different points on the chromosomes, with some spots on the genome differing as much as 1,000 per cent in rates at other points (high recombination rate regions are termed 'hotspots'). The result of this process is a genome that is made up of chromosomes divided into segments of DNA that represent different (but not all) paths through an individual's past genealogical tree, which we might sometimes refer to as their genomic ancestry.

Two areas of the genome, however, largely escape the effects of recombination because they are inherited from one parent only: the Y chromosome, inherited from the father, and the mitochondrial DNA (mtDNA), inherited from the mother. In humans some 90 per cent of the Y chromosome does not recombine (and thus is known as the non-recombining portion or the NRY). Only two small sections at each tip of the chromosome where there is sequence similarity with the X chromosome undergo recombination, and thus are known as pseudoautosomal regions. Similarly, the remainder of the X chromosome does not recombine in males (barring karyotypic anomalies, deviations from the normal number or structure of chromosomes), though it does in females. The Y chromosome contains very few genes compared to most autosomes and, as importantly, there is only one Y chromosome per cell. The genealogical tree constructed from the NRY represents a strictly paternal line of descent, and thus can be a useful marker of sex-specific demographic processes.

The second non-recombining region of the genome is mtDNA, which is a piece of circular haploid DNA that is inherited strictly along the maternal line. mtDNA is not contained in the nucleus as are the Y chromosome and other chromosomes, but rather within the energy-generating mitochondria of the cell. Different types of cells contain multiple mitochondria, ranging from a few hundred to many thousand, each with their own copy of the mtDNA genome. Though the mtDNA genome is very small (~16,000 base pairs), its relative abundance on a per-cell basis makes it easier to extract from long-dead samples even when degraded or broken. Some portions of the mtDNA genome also undergo fairly rapid mutation, making it a useful marker to distinguish changes in populations over time.

Replication is not always perfect. It may happen that an error takes place during meiosis such that the wrong nucleotide is incorporated into a replicating DNA strand, resulting in a variant in the nucleotide sequence compared to the parental version (i.e., a mutation). These alternate forms of a gene or sequence are termed alleles and can occur in recombinant DNA as well as in Y chromosome and mtDNA. The error may be fatal, preventing the survival of the fertilized egg. It might also result in some change in an inherited characteristic such as eye or skin colour, height, ability to digest certain chemicals such as lactose or greater immunity to specific diseases. However, the majority of mutations likely cause no identifiable effects on a new organism (i.e., they are neutral). In any case, the mutation is transmitted to offspring, and is ultimately the source of all genetic diversity. Alleles are fundamental to the study of population genetics because they are the primary markers of genealogical descent: individuals sharing the same sets of alleles are likely to share a common ancestor more recently. Moreover, since through the generations identical sections of DNA become increasingly broken up through recombination, the longer the segments of shared DNA, the more closely related individuals are. This likelihood is greater when many alleles, particularly those that are statistically uncommon (rare alleles), appear in multiple individuals. Essentially, population genetics and its historical version, genetic history, is the study of allele frequencies in populations, their changes over time and the relationships among populations sharing the same alleles.

Whether one is working with non-recombinant DNA from the Y chromosome or mtDNA or with recombinant nuclear DNA, for any of these types of DNA to be useful to historians, material must first be obtained from living or dead organisms. Then the base pairs or building blocks of the genome termed nucleotides must be put into its proper order. Then one must identify the variations at each single site in DNA at which one base has been exchanged for another (for example, cytosine for thymine or adenine for guanine). These inherited variations, termed single nucleotide polymorphisms or SNPs, as well as repeating sequences of one to six base pairs of DNA, termed microsatellites, form the basis of comparisons of individuals and populations. Simply stated, virtually all research in genetic history consists of the collection and sequencing of genetic samples, comparison of SNPs and microsatellites from these genetic samples with statistical models that predict divergence and commonality, and analysis of the results. While this may sound simple, it is fraught with technical, conceptual and interpretative problems, making genetic history no more objective than any other kind of historical research.

What samples?

The technical problems begin with the samples. As we saw above, most genetic history projects, including the 'out of Africa' and the Sally Hemings studies described above, work with contemporary DNA obtained from living subjects. The obvious advantage of using fresh DNA is that it is intact, largely free from contamination if collected and handled properly, and its source can be clearly established and controlled. For projects such as the Hemings investigation, working with contemporary DNA is the ideal approach. For studies of more distant historical processes, particularly for migration studies, the use of contemporary DNA can pose serious difficulties.

Before the advances discussed below in ancient DNA studies, one can understand the temptation to use modern populations to understand the past, but such an approach was and remains deeply problematic. We have seen that Kossinna assumed that certain skull types in twentieth-century Italy were likely evidence of sixth-century migration. The fact that thirteen hundred years of history had intervened between these two moments, including multiple military incursions from Germany into the Italian peninsula into the modern period, migrations of individuals and groups for land, for work or for other reasons, seemed to him irrelevant. Today, geneticists extrapolating from modern populations to the past seem to make the same assumptions. A study of the population of the British Isles assumes that if an individual has four grandparents from the same location, that person can be a proxy for the population of the region since the Anglo-Saxon invasions.[9] This retrospective approach rests on a number of assumptions. First and most obviously, it minimizes population movements, demographic events such as plagues, bottlenecks and replacements over more than a millennium. It may be that in some locations, population remained stable, but this must be demonstrated, not assumed. In places such as Hungary, almost total population replacements may have taken place a number of times.[10] Most areas probably fall between these extremes, but it us up to historians and scientists to find out the actual population history of a given region, not simply assume massive continuity.

A related problem with the data from modern DNA concerns sampling and locating. The better studies attempted to focus on individuals from small communities whose grandparents were known to have lived in the same villages. However, these SNPs thus obtained are often compared with standard databases of DNA compiled primarily for medical research that provide very coarsely grained geographical specificity, usually on a national scale. For example, the Population Reference Sample or POPRES, which is the database commonly used to examine diversity, contains some 6,000 subjects of African-American, east Asian, south Asian, Mexican and European origin. The European samples include data from 938 individuals of northern European origin collected in London and 2,809 collected in Lausanne.[11] These samples are organized geographically according to existing national frontiers, treating, say, DNA obtained from the French Département du Nord at the same level as those from Provence. Likewise, 'German DNA' in such databases lumps together DNA from the Rhineland, Bavaria and Saxony, while individuals from the Trentino and Naples are simply located as 'Italian'. Until much more finely grained DNA maps of Europe can be created, results obtained using such material is extremely dubious.

An even more fundamental problem when using modern DNA to understand historical processes is that, over time, as a result of factors such as genetic drift and the so-called founder effect (where a single individual's genetic material is disproportionately transmitted to future generations), an analysis of modern DNA is essentially a study of the 'winners' only. A modern DNA study thus may well miss the genetic diversity and the complexity of populations in the past. For geneticists interested primarily in the study of genetically linked diseases in modern populations, this is of course not a problem. However, for historians who wish to understand the difference between past and present, the use of modern DNA poses serious problems.

Thus, historians must be very clear about the questions that they wish to investigate and the likelihood that modern DNA can actually contribute to their research: those of us who are old enough to remember the heyday of quantitative history, with its at times exaggerated claims, will also remember the adage 'Garbage in, garbage out'.

Given these difficulties of using modern DNA to study ancient populations, it might seem logical to sequence ancient DNA (aDNA). By collecting aDNA from bones and teeth (as well as other less common preserved human remains), one avoids the need to use stand-ins for the subjects one wishes to study. Ideally, studies of ancient populations, migrations, relationships and so on should concentrate on the actual DNA of the individuals and groups under consideration, not their putative descendants. Unfortunately, the technical complexities of working with aDNA are even greater than those of working with modern DNA.

After death, the mechanisms that constantly repair DNA in a living organism cease to function and the DNA begins to break down. The exact rate depends on many factors, including temperature, humidity and the pH of the soil in which the remains are found. Until recently, a process known as PCR, or polymerase chain reaction, which came into use in the 1980s, was widely used to obtain sequence data from specific segments of the genome and to replicate it in thousands of copies for further research. PCR was a major step forward and made possible by extraordinary advances, including Svante Pääbo's sequencing of the Neanderthal genome in 1997. However, the process is complex and prone to error, and is usually applied to only portions of the genome, typically the mitochondria or portions of the Y chromosome This technique for resequencing and amplifying cannot produce sequences of more than 100–200 bp, and the amount of DNA that can be recovered is quite low and the process is time-consuming and expensive. Because cells, as we have seen, contain more copies of mtDNA than nuclear DNA, frequently if any useful DNA can be extracted using this method, it is only mtDNA, but even here PCR is plagued with a second problem: contamination.

Contamination is ubiquitous and inescapable. It begins with possible contact with other human remains after burial, continues with the handling of remains by archaeologists and curators, and finally with contamination by the very geneticists conducting the amplification and sequencing. Moreover, within labs where amplification of DNA is being carried out regularly, millions of molecules of amplified DNA are produced from each specimen, molecules that are so small that they pass through the most sophisticated air filters and are carried by contact with researchers, tools and equipment to other specimens. Even when specimens are thoroughly washed and irradiated, traces of contaminating DNA remain. An illustrative anecdote I was told by a senior geneticist is that initially scientists sequencing human DNA in Europe were astonished to find significant amounts of DNA that pointed to Asia, until it was realized that the gloves used to handle the samples had all been made in China.

Ancient DNA laboratories are rapidly overcoming the technical problems involved in amplifying and sequencing aDNA, but progress is slow and there is no consensus concerning best practice that satisfies all geneticists. In a provocative letter entitled 'Ancient DNA: Do It Right or Not at All', published a generation ago in *Science Magazine*, Alan Cooper of Oxford University and Hendrik N. Poinar of the Max Planck Institute for Evolutionary Biology listed nine key criteria that they considered essential routine good practice.[12] These included a physically isolated work area, control amplifications, appropriate molecular behaviour, reproducibility, cloning, biochemical preservation, quantitation, associated remains and, perhaps most important, independent replication. Until recently, few studies using aDNA met all of these criteria.

Fortunately, in 2005 a new process of massive parallel sequencing termed Next-Generation Sequencing (NGS) was developed and since 2010 has entered into wide use and transformed the possibilities of doing massive sequencing, even of very old samples, and in the process overcome many of the impediments to ancient DNA analysis. This process involves the fragmentation of the DNA samples into 200–500 bp fragments that are then separated and immobilized on a solid surface prior to sequencing. Then millions or even billions of fragments can be sequenced simultaneously. Moreover, it is possible to target specific regions or SNPs for specific research purposes. Analysis of NGS sequence data can actually make use of the weaknesses of aDNA, that is, contamination and degradation, to separate ancient DNA from contaminates. Those segments that are too long and in too good condition are recognized as contaminates. Likewise, 'errors' such as substitutions of one base where another might be expected, can be a marker of the normal degradation typical of aDNA and are retained for analysis.

However, even with the spectacular advances of NGS, recovery and analysis of aDNA remains highly problematic. Many portions of bone and teeth simply no longer contain much DNA. A fundamental breakthrough, almost equal to the development of NGS, was the 2015 discovery that a small bone attached to the skull that forms a portion of the inner ear, the petrous bone, the most dense part of the skeletal system, is particularly impervious to contamination or degradation.[13] Studies have found that while bones such as the parietal skull bone preserve on an average 2.2 per cent of endogenous DNA, and teeth, often used because of their better preservation, are likely to preserve 16.4 per cent, the petrous bone averages 40 per cent.[14] This extraordinary discovery has transformed the potential of using genomic analysis both for very ancient individuals and for comprehensive studies of whole communities. However, the same qualities of the petrous bone that make it ideal for population studies make it unsuitable for the study of other subjects such as pathogens. For these studies, one must rely on teeth or, for diseases such as leprosy, other less dense portions of the skeletal system.

Analysis

The actual sequencing of DNA, whether ancient or modern, is only the first challenge in using genetics to inform history. Sequencing produces simply a long string of letters indicating the order in which the bases A, G, C and T appear. In order to understand this process, we begin with a simple diagram that is a small part of the genetic profile of a woman who died in the village of Collegno, a few kilometres from the city of Turin, Italy, around the year 600.[15]

In this Sequence Alignment/Map file or SAM, the top line indicates where on the first chromosome this particular segment is located when aligned to the reference genome, which appears on the bottom line, the standard map of the human genome created by the Genome Reference Consortium (GRC), used to assemble fragments of genomic material resulting from next-generation sequencing. The coloured letters A, C, T and G indicate the order of the four bases, adenine (A), cytosine (C), guanine (G) and thymine

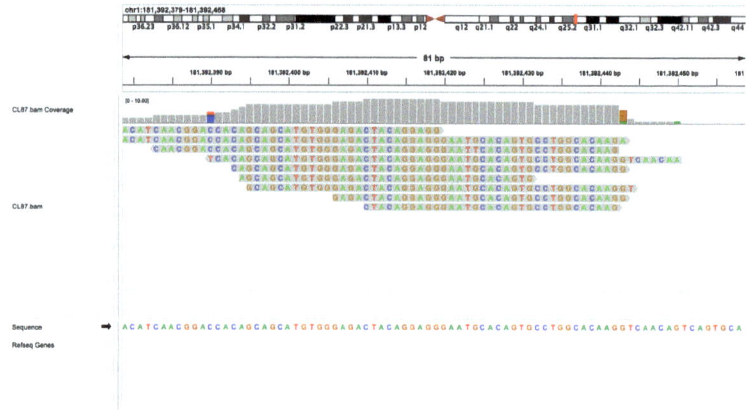

FIGURE 9 *Sequence alignment map of individual in Collegno grave CL 87. Reproduced with permission of Yijie Tian.*

(T), the fundamental elements of deoxyribonucleic acid or DNA, as they appear when processed by a sequencing machine.

With ancient DNA, as in this case, the success of the sequencing process is often incomplete and does not cover all the bases of the DNA fragment, so it is often necessary to replicate the process to increase the likelihood of obtaining complete coverage. In this example, we see nine versions of the read sequence, almost all of which match what would be expected from the reference genome. The exceptions are marked in the graph showing the coverage of each site. In the first one, three out of four reads are Cs, which corresponds to the reference genome, while in the fourth one, the sequencer read a T; in the second one, four times the sequencer read a G, while once it read an A. Such iterative processes are necessary to correct any errors in the sequencing process. On the other hand, in some cases, the read is not an error and may actually indicate that an individual carried a genetic variation in which, for example, thymine (T) replaced cytosine (C). These single nucleotide polymorphisms or SNPs are the basic elements of many genetic research studies, especially in the evolving discipline of genomic history.

How these SNPs can be used to establish relationships can be illustrated from another image of a portion of the mtDNA of three individuals who lived in Italy during the sixth century (Figure 10).

CR5 CAACTGCAACTCCAAAGCCACCCCTCACCACTAGGATACCAAC
RIV90 CAACTGCAACTCCAAAGTCACCCCTCACCACTAGGATACCAAC
PER4 CAACTGCAACTCCAAAGCCACCCCTCACCACTAGGATACCAAC

FIGURE 10 *Section of mtDNA of three individuals from sixth-century Italy.*

In order to make these strings of letters meaningful, we need to submit them to some sort of statistical analysis that will allow us to build models with the potential of helping to resolve historical questions.

With mtDNA and that portion of the Y chromosome that does not recombine in each generation, it is possible to establish genetic relationships along the male or female line. In the example above, we see one site at which two individuals have a cytosine base C, at a specific location, while the third has a thymine base (T). A mutation has occurred at some time, resulting in a greater distance between individuals CR5 and PER4 on the one hand and individual RIV90. The methodologies for calculating how these individuals might be related have long been known to population geneticists. Classic population genetics uses as a fundamental tool the Wright–Fisher model, which posits N individuals, each of which has two copies of each chromosome. It assumes that generations are non-overlapping and that at each generation, each chromosome inherits its genetic material from a uniformly chosen chromosome from the previous generation, independently from all other chromosomes. The simple version of the model omits many important details, including mutation, recombination, sexes, non-overlapping generations, population size changes, population structure, selection and so on, but is still useful in projecting forward in time. Great insight has been achieved from the Wright–Fischer model about how we expect genetics to behave, and similarly how genetic data should appear if the simple model held true.

While the Wright–Fisher model was developed to look forward in time, historians begin with DNA, either modern or ancient, and project backward in time to understand the processes that produced the observed population. This is possible by using coalescent theory as the basis for inferences, which is essentially the Wright–Fisher model with various assumptions relaxed in reverse. The coalescent considers how a sample of chromosomes from the present will be related through the past. If we trace the ancestry of a group of individuals backwards in time, the number of distinct lineages will decrease and eventually must reach one, that is, the Most Recent Common Ancestor (MRCA) through random sampling variance (i.e., some parents had more than one child, some had none). The advantage of the coalescent is running the process backwards in time simplifies the analysis since one does not need to consider individuals that did not contribute to the ancestry of the sample in the present.

As one works backward in time, it becomes evident that groups of individuals descended from the same distant ancestor share sets of alleles or SNPs on the same chromosome. These sets, termed haplotypes, make it possible to organize the whole human population into haplogroups. Worldwide studies of Y-chromosomal and mtDNA haplogroups have demonstrated a strong correlation between geographical location and haplogroups, such that one can estimate the relative frequency of haplotype by area. It does not follow that everyone in a specific region will belong to the same haplogroup, nor does it follow that everyone in a specific haplogroup has ancestors from the region in which it is most common, but it does provide a clue to the possible geographic origin of groups and possibly even individuals.

As powerful as coalescent studies may be for determining population history, it only works for the non-recombinant portion of the DNA. The problem with such an approach, however, is that the study of non-recombinant DNA provides only one very small portion of an individual's genealogy. Every person has two parents, four grandparents, eight great-grandparents, sixteen great-great-grandparents, and so on. A single lineage becomes quite trivial within the entire genetic make-up of an individual after just a few generations. Thus, understanding the complexity of dynamic populations runs into serious problems with this approach. In historical studies, moreover, it tends to simplify and homogenize populations, erasing the multiple possibilities and complexities that make up the human past. As one geneticist put it, it is like reading a single page of a 500-page book and trying to write a summary of the book.

Ideally, then, one should study not only the non-recombinant Y chromosome and mtDNA but also the recombinant DNA that is found in the cell nucleus. This DNA contains evidence of the total ancestry of an individual and thus potentially provides a much richer source for understanding the population history of an individual or group. However, the problems of recombinant DNA transform the problem of creating genealogies and population histories. Now we are not building a tree that represents a single genealogy, but instead, one must imagine an Ancestor Recombination Graph or ARG (coalescent with recombination).[16]

Since every diploid genome sequence contains hundreds of thousands of independent loci, each with its own most recent common ancestor, calculation of such graphs becomes extremely complex. Introducing recombination not only included these problems, but now adds the complexity of considering all the different ways edges can be added and removed from the graph. After one or two of these recombination events, the inferential problem (i.e., working out a likelihood function that relates mutation data to the recombination graph to the underlying population history) quickly becomes very difficult to the point of being intractable without major approximations.

Because recombination exists, in theory this means that as we move along the sequence, each nucleotide could possess a different genealogy. The two genealogies between neighbouring nucleotides could be different but will be correlated (i.e., will be more similar than you would expect by chance). In reality, recombination is unlikely to have occurred enough within the history of a population such that every nucleotide has a different genealogy, and so groups of neighbouring nucleotides (or loci) may very well be essentially represented by a single genealogy (1,000 bp is a reasonable size such that the effect of recombination can be ignored). Neighbouring loci will still be correlated, but if we pick loci that are far enough away from each other, these loci can essentially be considered independent. Thus, picking a set of independent loci from across the genome that individually can be captured by a single genealogy can be used to make inferences about population history analogous to the idea of running the population history experiment many, many times, as each independent loci is essentially a different realization of the evolutionary process based on the same underlying history.

Thus, examining many independent loci allows us to assess the probability of the set of genealogies inferred from the mutation data given a single underlying population history. As such one can also find the population history that *best* explains the mutation data.

Likewise, because even with recombination, long stretches of DNA remain the same, in each generation, population geneticists can infer relationships by identifying identical long blocks of nuclear DNA. The longer such similar blocks are, the more closely related the individuals are. This is called 'identity by descent', or IBD. The importance of IBD will become clear when we look at its application in historical research.

This basic review of genetics may seem elementary, but social scientists and humanists need to understand what genetic data actually is, how it is collected and how it is manipulated to reconstitute the genetic background of individuals and communities, just as we must understand the nature of written and material sources, their transmission and the appropriate tools by which they can be analysed. We will turn now to some of those tools used by geneticists to interrogate genetic data.

3

Making Sense of Genomic Data

Assuming that we have successfully obtained fairly accurate sequence data as in the example from the previous chapter, we are still a long way from being able to draw any historical information from these long strings of As, Cs, Ts and Gs. Population geneticists have developed a number of sophisticated statistical procedures to analyse these strings in order to understand population structure. As we have seen in the previous chapter, it is possible to use a variation of the Wright–Fischer model to work backwards, tracing mutations in a population through generations to the individuals that coalesce in the most recent common ancestor, with all of his or her descendants sharing the same genotype. Individuals sharing hundreds or even thousands of the same mutations or alleles are said to belong to the same mtDNA or Y-chromosome haplogroup. Moreover, since people naturally reproduce with people who are geographically nearby, over time there is a general correspondence between the probability of a particular haplogroup and geography.

Human population can be divided into three groups. They are first the L haplogroups (number L0 to L8), which are most common in Africa and contain the most genetic diversity. Outside of Africa, two major groups exist: M, common in eastern Eurasia, and N, which are two separate lineages of African haplogroup L3. By tracing common alleles, these macro-haplogroups are further divided into numerous sub-groups that share groups of specific alleles unique to them that indicate more recent common ancestors than those of the mega-groups. For example, macrohaplogroup M can be subdivided into haplogroups C, D, E, G, Q and Z, as well as groups lettered with M. Haplogroups named after the remaining letters of the English alphabet have been placed within macro-haplogroup N. Each of these has a unique common female ancestor, although they also share more distant common ancestors until they reach the founder of the three mega-groups and, ultimately, the so-called mitochondrial Eve, the common female ancestor of all humans.

Similarly, all Y-chromosomal haplogroups ultimately coalesce in the most common recent Y ancestor or the Y-chromosomal Adam. However, across time genetic mutations have produced a great number of more defined haplogroups that geographically divide among Africa, east Asia, south-east Asia, south Asia, north Asia, central/east Asia, Oceania, the Americas and Europe.[1] In order to avoid confusion, the Y Chromosome Consortium established a nomenclature system in which major haplogroups are designated by capital letters (A–T) and then sub-groups are identified by combinations of lower-case letters and numbers. Finally, the haplogroup's name may be followed by the specific SNP that characterizes the haplogroup.[2] As a result of migration, exchange and intermarriage, there are over twenty distinct Y-chromosomal haplogroups in Europe today, the most common being R1b-M269 in western Europe, I1-Mw53 in Scandinavia, I2-M438 in the Balkans and eastern Europe, and R1a-M420 in eastern Europe.[3]

Archeogeneticists wishing to understand ancient population structures can find these haplogroups useful, particularly in looking at the complexities of populations. In a recent study of Avar-period cemeteries in central Hungary, for example, our team found only two Y-chromosomal haplogroups among 279 individuals buried in the cemetery of Rákóczifalva, while this cemetery contained individuals from some forty mtDNA haplogroups. This suggests that the community was strictly patrilocal, with two male lineages that sought external partners from a wide spectrum of kindreds.[4]

However, neither mtDNA nor Y-chromosome haplogroups are very helpful in understanding the full complexity of one's ancestry and thus of populations. As we have seen, these markers tell us very little about the complex ancestry and are not very helpful in understanding whole populations. After all, the entire human genome contains over three billion loci, each of which could, in theory, undergo recombination and thus, in theory, have its own ancestry (although in fact, as we shall see, large tracts of DNA tend to remain whole in each generation, only gradually breaking down into ever smaller segments). The possibility of calculating ancestry at that scale calls for very different statistical methods than those used to identify haplogroups. For that, we need a way to study the nuclear DNA, that portion which is inherited from all of one's ancestors, but which is subject to recombination in each generation.

Principal Component Analysis

One of the most commonly applied, and most easily misunderstood when presented to a general audience, population genetics tools is Principal Component Analysis.[5] This is a statistical procedure that identifies patterns in a complex dataset by simplifying it into a smaller and more manageable set that still retains significant patterns. Technically, it is an unsupervised statistical procedure in that it does not provide pre-labelled data but simply allows the raw data to organize themselves. It does this by converting a set of possibly correlated variables into a set of those components that account for as much of the variance within the set as possible. The procedure encodes the genetic data numerically to represent the number of copies of a particular allele at each SNP. A matrix showing the covariance or tendency in the linear relationship between variables is constructed to represent the relationships between all pairs of individuals sampled. A mathematical procedure calculates the characteristic or eigenvectors for this matrix. These eigenvectors become the principal components and their corresponding characteristic values indicate the amount of variation that is explained by each principal component. Thus, the first component accounts for the greatest variance, the second for the second greatest, and so on. Principal component analyses can in theory be used to follow any number of components. However, in genetics it is frequently used to create a visual representation of genetic distance and relationships separating individuals or populations. For this, the first and second principal components are used to plot each individual on a two-dimensional x–y axis. The result is to show, in a simple image, the relative distance separating all of the samples.[6]

PCA has been used by geneticists since the pioneering work of Cavalli-Sforza,[7] but perhaps the most famous use of PCA in recent years was by John Novembre, who plotted the genomes of 1,387 contemporary Europeans collected and genotyped as part of the Population Reference Sample project or POPRES. These were individuals whose European country of origin of each of their grandparents was known, or at least their own reported country of birth. From each, he focused on 197,146 SNPs or loci on their genomes.[8] He then used PCA analysis to situate each individual relative to all of the others along a two-dimensional axis. Based only on the first two principal components, the data arranged themselves such that the resulting two-dimensional visual summary produced an extraordinarily accurate map of Europe, even though no geographical data had been included. Novembre concluded that distance, rather than any other factor, was the most significant component of genetic identity between individuals and populations.

Historians, archaeologists and geneticists working with ancient DNA have adopted the same approach to identify population groupings in the historical communities that they study. Because we do not have sufficient numbers of high-coverage ancient sequences from across Eurasia, they plot the principal components separating their samples against a modern population dataset. The latter is necessary because ancient sequences lack the deep coverage of modern DNA and often lack specific SNPs, and thus one needs more complete samples, those of modern individuals, to help match the SNPs that can be recovered from the ancient samples.

The results can be significantly informative, but they can also be misleading. First, the validity of the PCA depends to a great extent on the quality of the modern sample used as background. The Population Reference Sample (POPRES) database used by John Novembre was originally compiled in 2005 for the purpose of pharmacogenetics research and combined ten different genetics databases. The European samples included 938 northern Europeans whose genetic data had been collected in London and 2,809 individuals collected in Lausanne. The information on their place of origin and that of their parents and grandparents was self-reported and limited to country of birth.[9] In subsequent studies, other modern databases have been used instead of POPRES, including the 1000 Genomes Project, which reconstructed the genomes of 2,504 individuals from twenty-six populations,[10] the Simons Genome Diversity Project[11] and the commercially developed Axiom Genome-Wide Origins chip.[12] Each of these databases has its advantages and disadvantages, depending on the procedures by which genomes were collected, the density of sampling from specific areas, and the ways that samples are classified for purposes of analysis.

In a recent study we examined the burials in a sixth-century cemetery to determine whether it might be possible to recognize genetic complexity within small communities located in northern Italy and in what is modern Hungary.[13] When we plotted our sixth-century samples against modern datasets compiled from POPRES, the 1000 Genomes Project and the Simons Genomic Diversity Project, to create a modern genetic map of Europe, we were able to recognize a spectrum along north–south axis groups.

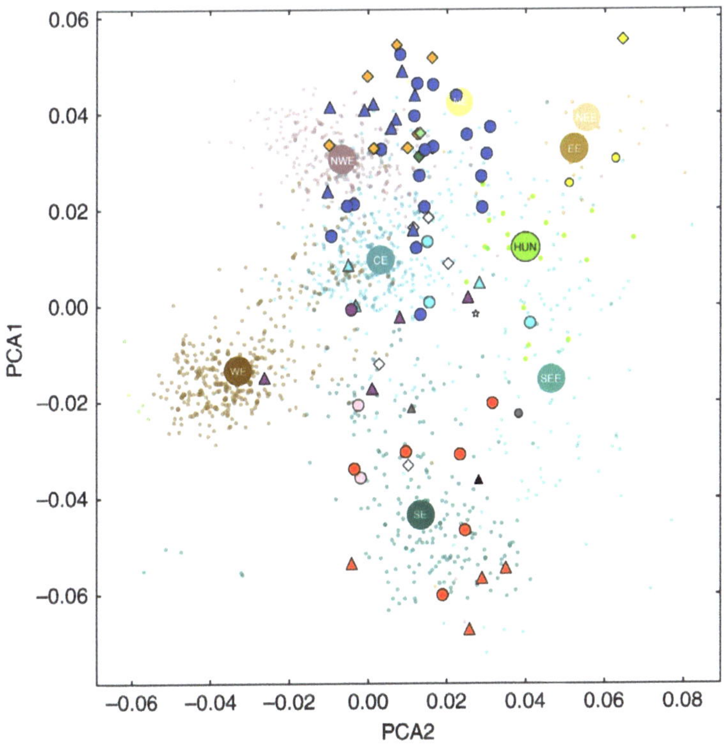

FIGURE 11 *PCA of burials at Szólád, Hungary, with Procrustes PCA of modern Europeans. Amorim et al., 'Understanding 6th-Century Barbarian Social Organization', fig. 2. Available under a CC BY 4.0 license.*

To interpret this PCA plot, one must understand that the small, background dots are the way that the samples from the 1000 Genome Project have arranged themselves based on the first two principal components that account for their differences. Then the coloured circles and triangles are our sixth-century individuals that have arranged themselves in relationship to the background individuals. The first falls generally in what today would be northern and central Europe. The second, were they contemporary individuals, would appear to be Italians. Neither group coincides with the contemporary population of Hungary. However, this visualization can be easily misinterpreted. Since the map produces clusters from our sixth-century site that map to northern Europe and one to southern Europe, one might erroneously conclude that these individuals, or their ancestors, came from either northern or southern Europe. This is by no means a necessary conclusion. We do not yet know what a detailed principal component plot of sixth-century Europe would look like. The fact that these groups fall north and south today should not be interpreted at first glance as evidence of migration from these regions. It is only evidence at this point of a differentiation between these two groups. Nor are the boundaries of these groups fixed. Depending on what percentage of ancestry from one or the other group one uses as the cut-off, one might draw the borders between the two groups differently, or even introduce additional groupings. The modern data help us to recognize groups but not their origins in the past, when a genetic map of Europe might have looked quite different.

Because of the problems associated with the use of modern datasets as background, as more and more ancient genomes become available, scientists are creating background datasets composed of roughly contemporary individuals against which to compare the populations that they wish to study. This promises a more accurate understanding of past populations, but it is contingent upon having adequate numbers of high-quality genomes from across the world. Even for Europe, where the vast majority of ancient genomes have been collected, serious lacunae exist, including virtually all of France as well as much of southern Europe. Thus, for example, in a recent paper published in *PNAS* that compared the results using both a modern and a pene-contemporaneous dataset, in the latter, it was not possible to differentiate between Italy and Iberia.[14] Much remains to be done to overcome such limitations.

Admixture analysis

Principal Component Analysis can be effective at showing structures in population and ordering this geographically, but it does not explain the underlying reasons for these structures. Differences that appear along the x and y axes of a PCA plot are the result of complex mixtures of genetic histories, but other methods are needed to discover what these mixtures are. All Europeans are the result of admixtures, some that took place in the very deep past, such as the triad of Palaeolithic Hunter-Gatherers, Neolithic farmers from Anatolia and Bronze Age Steppe Herders. Others took place more recently. In order to estimate the various ancestry mixtures within a population, geneticists have developed a number of procedures to estimate the various genetic backgrounds that combine in a specific individual. Various commercial packages use a variation of a method termed admixture analysis or model-based clustering analysis, which is a supervised statistical procedure to identify and quantify the different genetic components from a variety of reference populations in ancient individuals.

Determining the significance of different ancestry components both within a population and between populations relies on a series of statistical procedures. Most important are F-statistics, a set of statistical tools that compare the amount of genetic variation both within and between populations.[15]

To accomplish this, one first needs to define reference populations. Usually, these are modern populations which, although themselves highly heterogeneous, shared sufficient alleles that have proven to be statistically valid to distinguish between different population groups. These ancestry informative markers or AIMs tend to be geographically distinguished, again because as populations intermarry certain alleles become more common within a geographical area. The 1000 Genome Project, whose database is frequently used for admixture analysis, divides the world's population into twenty-six populations which are in turn grouped into five 'super populations': African, European, south Asian, east Asian, American.[16] The populations include African ancestry in the southwestern United States; Caribbean African in Barbados; Bengali in Bangladesh; British from England and Scotland; Chinese from Dai in Xishuangbanna, China; Colombians in Medellín, Colombia; Esan in Nigeria; Finnis in Finland; Gambians in Western Division

– Mandinka; Gujarati Indians in Houston, Texas, United States; Han Chinese in Beijing, China; Han Chinese from south China; Iberian populations in Spain; Indian Telugu in the UK; Japanese in Tokyo, Japan; Kinh in Ho Chi Minh City, Vietnam; Luhya in Webuye, Kenya; Mende in Sierra Leone; Mexican Ancestry in Los Angeles, CA, United States; Peruvians in Lima, Peru; Puerto Ricans in Puerto Rico; Punjabi in Lahore, Pakistan; Sri Lankan Tamils in the UK; Tuscans in Italy; Yoruba in Ibadan, Nigeria; Utah residents with northern and western European ancestry from the CEPH collection. While useful, there is much to be wary of when using these constructed populations as reference. In particular one should note the mixture of geographical and ethnic labels as well as the use of descendants of enslaved Africans as proxies for Africans.

In archeogenomic publications, these groups will frequently be represented by different colours in charts that will indicate admixture proportions, as seen in Figure 12.

FIGURE 12 *A typical admixture table in European archeogenomic publications.*

One should not read this to suggest that everyone in these areas shares an identical genetic background: these are approximate estimates of the most common genetic background based on specific AIMs. In each of these populations, while they have great similarity overall, there are significant differences among individuals, and each could be subdivided into still more discrete units. In fact, there is greater differentiation within a given population, however it is defined, than between populations.

Taking these somewhat arbitrary populations as background, software programs such as ADMIXTURE and RFMix use algorithms to estimate the ancestry proportions for each individual sampled.[17] These programs must be run repeatedly, assuming different numbers of ancestral populations each time, in order to find the optimal model that can characterize the individual genome with a limited subset of ancestry populations. These can then be represented in a triangle graph or bar graph that shows proportionally the admixture of each ancestry.

A triangle graph is most useful when positing that an individual has three source populations. For example, a hypothetical individual whose ancestry was 70 per cent central European (CEU), 20 per cent central Italian (TSI) and 10 per cent Finnish FIN) is illustrated in Figure 13.

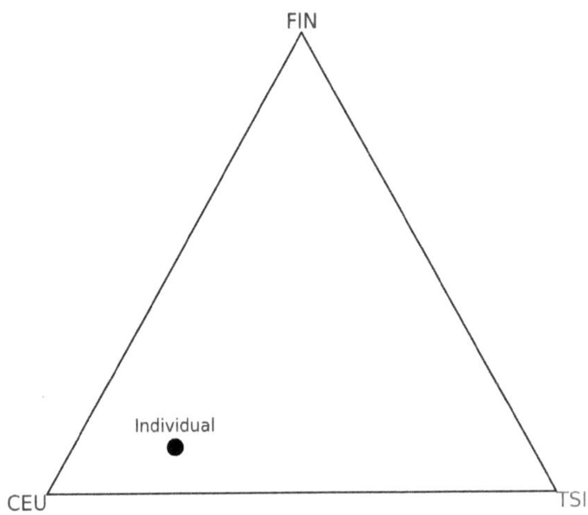

FIGURE 13 *Admixture triangle plot showing three hypothetical components of an individual's ancestry.*

If more than three populations are used to model admixture, a bar graph is more appropriate, and one will frequently see admixture bar graphs in the following chapters. Ancestry analysis is very useful in identifying the underlying ancestries of individuals, but depending on the background datasets being used, it can also be problematic. The 1000 Genome dataset lacks sufficient fine-grained differentiation to uncover accurately the small but significant differences in populations that are quite similar. For example, since its European datasets are simply Iberian, Tuscan, Finnish, Great Britain and central European, one cannot distinguish between northern and southern Italy or any of the populations across all of Continental Europe north of the Alps. Nor can one be certain, when using the 1000 Genome database, that the distributions of ancestries in the past were the same as it is today. A recent publication of the admixture of a western Hungarian cemetery from the mid-sixth century, for example, produced the result seen in Figure 14.

But what exactly does this mean? It does *not* mean that any of the individuals buried in this cemetery had their origins in Finland, Great Britain, the Iberian Peninsula or Tuscany. All that our *admixture* analysis shows is that in comparison to a modern population, our sixth-century individuals present a mixture of several genetic ancestry components, but that within this particular

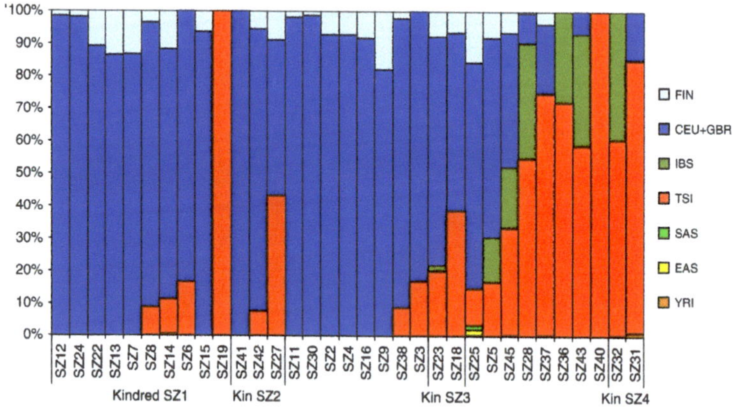

FIGURE 14 *Admixture graph of the Szólád cemetery. Amorim et al., 'Understanding 6th-Century Barbarian Social Organization', fig. 3. Available under a CC BY 4.0 license.*

population two such components predominate, components that, if they were modern individuals, we would assume had genetic origins in central to northern Europe or in central northern Italy respectively based on the predetermined populations in the model. In this case, all that we can establish is the complexity of our populations and the reality that two very general groups can be recognized within this complexity, not the origins of these groups themselves.

Because of the lack of definition within these large modern databases and the uncertainty of the extent to which they are applicable to past populations, archeogeneticists are attempting to accumulate sufficiently large databases of ancient genomes to define populations based on AIMs found in populations roughly contemporary to those that they wish to study.[18] This process, too, is fraught with problems and must be managed carefully. Creating such databases requires the consolidation of data from many studies by different research teams. Some, unaware of the problematic nature of ethnic labels we discussed above, have labelled their samples with ethnic denominators that lack justification. This practice, common not only in ancient DNA studies but also in medical research, is deeply problematic and has been the object of considerable discussion.[19] These must be replaced with geographical and chronological labels that do not presuppose an imputed ethnic identity. A second problem that arises with using ancient DNA is the quality of the data itself. Modern databases provide high coverage whole-genome sequencing data of a large number of samples for each group. Ancient DNA databases contain some whole genome sequences, but many are SNP arrays, and thus do not cover the entire genome. Moreover, the data is typically of low coverage, fragmented, and shows both post-mortem damage and contamination. Because of the low coverage, sequencing often captures only one of the two chromosomes inherited from parents. Thus, while using ancient DNA datasets for admixture analysis as well as for PCA plotting, it is often not yet possible to achieve the resolution that one would ideally want. For example, Figure 15 (which we will see again when we discuss the effects of the Langobard conquest of Italy) shows the results of admixture analysis from the same Italian cemetery, now with additional samples. The first used the 1000 Genome Project database, the second a pene-contemporary database created by the authors

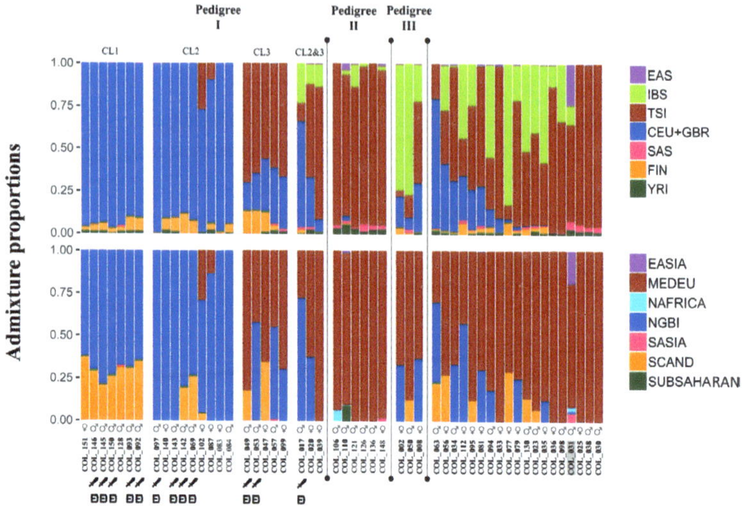

FIGURE 15 *Admixture graphs of Collegno burials. The top uses modern populations; the bottom, contemporary populations. Tian, Koncz, Defant et al., 'The role of emerging elites', fig. 2. Available under a CC BY 4.0 license.*

Comparing the two, one finds that the Scandinavian component is more significant in the panel using ancient DNA, which is probably more representative. However, the quality of the pene-contemporary panel was not powerful enough to distinguish between Iberian and Italian datasets so they were combined into a single population (MEDEU). Much remains to be done to refine usable datasets that can overcome these challenges.

Inferring biological kinship

Model-based clustering methods assume that individuals are random samples from one or more populations, and thus that the probability that two individuals share any particular allele at a SNP is a simple function of that allele's frequency in the general population. As such, these methods implicitly assume that pairs of individuals may be from the same population, but are not closely related.

A different model is necessary if one wishes to untangle closer relationships (i.e., what might be described as biological kinship relations in population genetics), such as parent/offspring, sibling, cousin relationships, and so on. Traditionally, archaeologists and physical anthropologists have attempted to identify kinship relationships among individuals buried in the same graveyard through such physical characteristics as the morphology of the frontal sinus, unusual dental traits that are often inherited or similar grave goods or nearby burials. However, such assumptions are speculative and at best might suggest a biological relationship without specifying the exact nature of that relationship.

With modern, high-coverage genomic data where confidently identified diploid genotypes – that is, those that show the two chromosomes inherited respectively from each parent – can be ascertained, determining close biological relationships is fairly straightforward and routine in genetics. The goal is to determine whether two individuals share zero, one, or two alleles (either SNPs or haplotypes) that are identical-by-descent (another IBD). The proportion of the genome that is IBD 0, 1 or 2 then allows the calculation of a kinship coefficient, the value of which is indicative of the specific type of relationship (for example, siblings have a kinship coefficient of 0.5). This is how companies like 23andMe can find relatives and how paternity testing works.

However, for ancient DNA, plagued as it is by low coverage sequence data, this is problematic. One often cannot see both alleles that an individual possesses due to low coverage, let alone see the same two alleles for two individuals. The data appear as haploid or single-strand DNA, although of course the DNA had been diploid. Population geneticists working with ancient genomic data overcome this limitation in a variety of ways. One is through developing statistical tools that generate what are called 'pseudo-haploid' data by sampling just one allele per SNP and then imputing the original diploid genotypes using modern reference panels.[20] An approach developed in the laboratory of Krishna Veeramah uses genotype likelihoods to estimate kinship parameters.[21] This method can account for uncertainty and accurately calculate the kinship coefficient that can infer relationships down to approximately fifth-degree relatives (depending on the quality of the underlying data), that is, for example, to third cousins. Veeramah's algorithm goes beyond simply identifying connections. By considering the

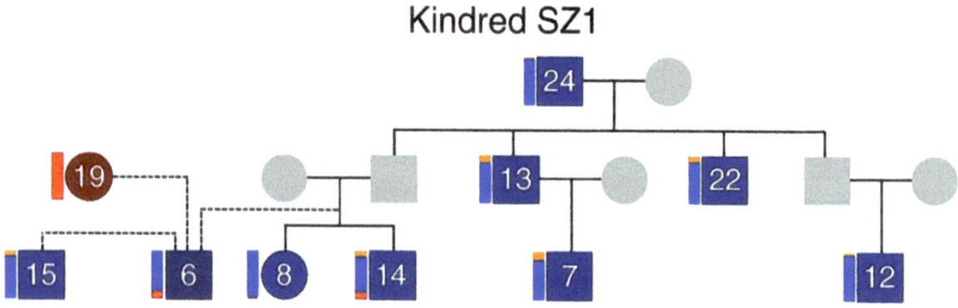

FIGURE 16 *Three generation pedigree from Szólád. Amorim et al., 'Understanding 6th-Century Barbarian Social Organization', fig. 4. Available under a CC BY 4.0 license.*

percentage of the c-kinship coefficient shared, it can determine the proximity of the relationship. When this is added to information about age and sex, it is possible to infer detailed biological pedigrees of kin groups (see Figure 16).

In this example, males are represented as squares, females by circles. The colours indicate the major admixture component while the bar graphs show the more detailed admixture of each. Grey circles and squares are individuals who must have been part of the pedigree but for whom we do not have genomic data. Thus, we see a male (twenty-four) who was the father of both thirteen and twenty-two. We can also infer that he was the grandfather of six, seven, eight, twelve and fourteen, even though we do not have genomic data from either the wife of twenty-four or many of the individuals in the second generation. However, alone, the algorithm is not capable of determining the actual structure of the kin group without additional, non-genetic information. Consider the example from a fifth-century Hungarian site shown in Figure 17.

As powerful as this technique is, one can see that it is not perfect: it can recognize relationships, as between HAC_4 and HAC_24 in this example, but alone it cannot determine which is the grandparent and which the grandchild. The determination that twenty-four is the child had to be made through osteological analysis that demonstrated that twenty-four was a child.

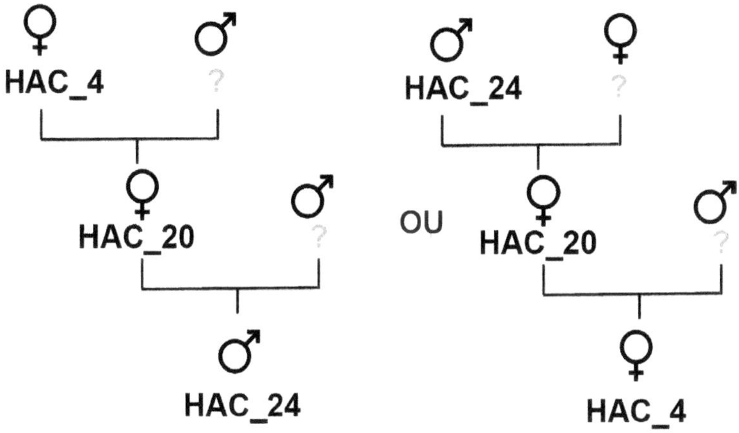

FIGURE 17 *Two different possible ways of constructing the same pedigree from Hács, Hungary. Reproduced with permission of István Koncz.*

Identity by descent

PCA and admixture procedures can suggest broad categories of ancestry, and tools like READ and lcMLkin can identify close biological kinship connections. A different procedure is necessary to identify significant but more distant biological relationships. A number of commercial software packages are able to identify more distant connections by tracing shared segments of modern DNA from a common ancestor. This is because, as we have seen, in each generation, a child inherits portions of each of the parent's chromosomes, as shown in Figure 18.

The top row indicates three couples, each with their chromosomes differently coloured. In each subsequent generation, the children will inherit portions of recombinant chromosomes of their parents. The third generation will in turn inherit portions of the chromones of their parents and hence also of their grandparents. The similarly coloured segments (as, in this case, the orange) indicates the segment that is identical by descent, demonstrating that both of these individuals inherited a portion of their genome from a common

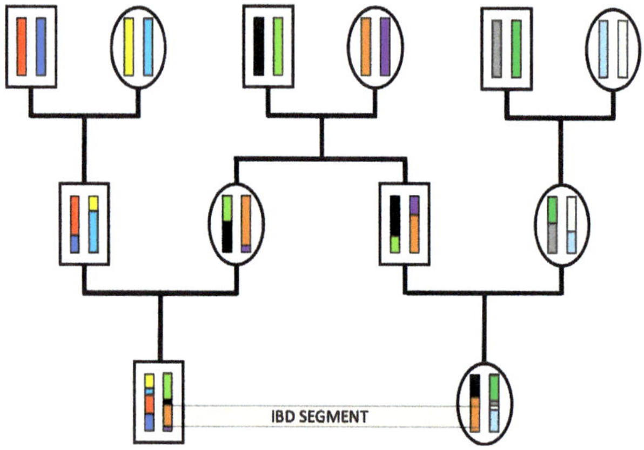

FIGURE 18 *IBD segments in a hypothetical pedigree of twelve individuals. Reproduced with permission of Krishna Veeramah.*

grandfather. The more recent the common ancestor of two individuals is, the longer the stretches of identical DNA, termed runs of homozygosity or ROH. Indeed, this is how commercial genetic testing companies such as 23andme or AncestryDNA identify connections among distant relatives.

Doing the same with ancient DNA is more challenging since the coverage is usually very poor, samples are contaminated and post-mortem degradation introduces genotyping errors. Very recently, however, in a series of papers, Harald Ringbauer and his colleagues have developed a means of accurately detecting identity-by-descent segments even in ancient DNA.[22] The tool that Ringbauer and his associates have created, ancIBD, overcomes the problems that haunt ancient DNA analysis. Using this method, it is now possible to identify with confidence IBD segments in samples with poor coverage (as low as 0.25x) and to do so not only using whole genome sequences but also the 1240k SNP arrays commonly captured by ancient DNA labs. This new tool makes it possible to identify biological relatedness up to the sixth degree and genealogical relationships even more distant reaching back as far as ten or even twenty generations, although for such distant connections it is impossible to determine the exact relationship. However, by analysing the lengths of shared segments, it is also roughly possible to determine the number of generations separating two individuals and thus to produce a rough timeline, since there is a recombination event each generation with the result that the smaller the IBD segments, the more distant the relationship. The relative distance between genes on a chromosome is measured in centimorgans (cM). One centimorgan is equal to a 1 per cent chance that two loci on a chromosome will be separated from each other due to recombination. The further removed two individuals are, the more recombination events will have taken place and thus the lower the centimorgan value. Using a tool such as ancIBD, geneticists can identify IBD segments shared across the generations. Very small amounts of IBD are likely to be shared widely in a population, making it difficult to find any meaningful connections across individuals or populations. However, by running different scenarios that screen the results for a specific number of centimorgans, the geneticist can fine-tune the results to show meaningful connections. Thus, for example, segments longer than 20cM mean that the individuals shared a common ancestor within 200 to 300 years. Still longer IBDs will indicate even closer timeframes.

IBD analyses are extremely useful in archeogenetics for a number of reasons. The rate of shared IBD segments can help determine the size of a population: large populations, such as those during the Roman Empire, typically have very few long-shared segments because of the wide potential mating pool. As populations shrink, the lengths of shared segments increase, since individuals within a smaller population are not only mating with closer relatives, but are likely to have multiple shared ancestors. Chronologically close but geographically distant IBD segments are very useful, when combined with isotopic and other analyses, to indicate migration events. Furthermore, examining IBD networks that connect different communities can indicate patterns of exogamy and endogamy within societies. Finally, by examining different IBD networks created by Y chromosomes and mtDNA, one can recognize gender-specific patterns of social cohesion and differentiation.

In Figure 19, from Joscha Gretzinger's study of population changes related to the Slavic expansion, for example, we see a network showing all pairs of ancient individuals in his study that share IBD segments longer than twelve cM. The early medieval individuals from northern Europe and Britain form a loose cluster, while those from the Slavic period from what is now Croatia, Poland, northwestern Ukraine and eastern Germany plot together. The pedigree

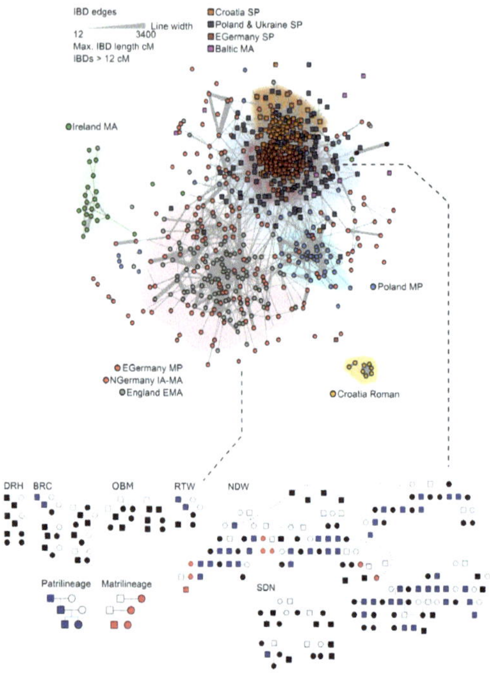

FIGURE 19 *IBD connections among populations before and after the Slavic expansion. Gretzinger et al., 'Ancient DNA Connects Large-Scale Migration with the Spread of Slavs', Extended data fig. 10. Available under a CC BY 4.0 license.*

reconstructions indicate the shift from small to large, patrilineally-oriented pedigrees in eastern Germany after the seventh century.

New and evolving methodologies

While admixture analysis, principal component analysis, biological kinship analysis and identity-by-descent networks are the most commonly encountered tools being used to uncover past population structures and movements, numerous other technologies contribute to aDNA analysis. FSTruct quantifies variability in population structure,[23] while tools such as IBDNe estimate effective population size by using IBD segments.[24] The average time of admixture can be calculated using tools such as Linkage Disequilibrium[25] or DATES v.753.[26] These and many more specialized statistical procedures uncover patterns in genomic datasets.

Moreover, new approaches and methods are being developed that promise further, more precise differentiation of patterns invisible when using standard methodologies. To cite but one example, a recent, novel methodology termed Twigstats developed by Leo Speidel and his colleagues at the Francis Crick Institute is being applied in order to overcome the challenge that in many regions ancestries are so similar that they are virtually indistinguishable using current methodologies.[27] It promises to improve the statistical power of the methods discussed above by focusing on recent coalescences of ancestries. This statistical procedure is an unsupervised tool that allows the computation of the ratio of variances among multiple samples (*f*-statistics) in a manner that determines an upper date threshold and focuses only on the younger branches. The result potentially allows for a time-stratified ancestry analysis that can provide a fine-scale differentiation within populations that are so similar that traditional methodologies cannot distinguish among them. Although at a preliminary state of application, this methodology promises to allow even greater disaggregation of early populations and provide insight into subtle admixtures of populations within fairly close timeframes.

By way of example, Speidel and his colleagues applied Twigstats to analyse 1,556 early medieval individuals. Among other findings, they were able to identify previously undetected evidence of individuals with Scandinavian ancestry already in the first century CE as well as the presence of individuals in what would become Norway, whose ancestry derives from Iron Age Britain. While this study relied exclusively on genomic data and did not attempt to anchor their samples in specific archaeological contexts, when combined with other disciplines, this approach will likely provide new levels of chronological and geographical precision.

Conclusions

In each of these statistical operations, we see that we are dealing with imperfect tools: the databases that we use are incomplete. The decision about which genetic markers to study prejudices the possible results we can obtain. The statistical tools that we use necessarily simplify our data, discarding much of it. And finally, the statistical modelling applied to genetics necessarily oversimplifies the complexity of human genetic history. George Box famously observed, 'Essentially, all models are wrong, but some are useful.' We must keep in mind that the models that we use to analyse our genomic data are indeed wrong, just as are the models derived from material culture, physical anthropology, isotopic analysis or written documentation. None adequately and perfectly captures the totality of the past. Given such limitations, historians who wish to understand the complex history of past populations cannot ignore genomic data, but the tentative models that population genetics produces from this data must be confronted with other models produced from cultural archaeology, isotopic studies and, yes, from the written record where possible, in order to comprehend the human past.

In each of the cases that we shall see in the next chapter, the genomic data alone would have been useless to understand the social and cultural complexities of early medieval societies. Archaeology is essential not only to provide the bones used in analyses, but also to provide detailed analyses of the organization of each cemetery, the grave goods associated with each individual, the depth and characteristics of each grave, and to work with population geneticists to see how patterns in material culture may intersect with models developed from genomic analysis. Isotopic analysis, quite independent of genetic analysis, is necessary to build models of diet, health and mobility, models that could then be compared with those developed from genetics. Historians, working with early medieval law codes as well as with narratives of the fifth and sixth centuries, are challenged to test rhetorical and ideological presentations of past societies against the complex models that appear from the genetics and the archaeology.

4

Ancient DNA and the Early Medieval Transition

Increasingly, research laboratories across Europe and North America are making use of the methods discussed above to better understand the dramatic changes that took place at the end of the Roman Empire. Not all of these projects have followed the same protocols. Few are truly interdisciplinary teams that fully integrate archaeological, anthropological, isotopic and historical data into what are essentially analyses of genetic data. Likewise, most have taken the approach of transect studies and have chosen to select samples extensively in space and time rather than intensively analysing in a comprehensive manner the complexities of whole cemeteries. Too often, the labelling of their data mixes ethnic and geographical categories, a problem which, as we have seen in Chapter 1, risks mixing ethnic and genetic categories. Nevertheless, preliminary results are beginning to emerge that show the complexity of the European population from Late Antiquity to the Middle Ages.

Rewriting history through genomes

In general, genetic approaches to the period of transition between Late Antiquity and the Early Middle Ages have focused on broad, long-term images of European populations, although some fine-grained regional studies are beginning to appear.

Several recent studies have begun to focus on populations in the Roman world. At the macro-level, these studies tend to emphasize continuity within the European population over the past 3,000 years.

A study of 127 ancient individuals from Rome and central Italy in 2019 conducted by Margaret Antonio and colleagues looked at shifts in population from roughly 3500 BCE until today.[1] They found that, during the height of the Roman Empire, the city's population was characterized primarily by a population with strong Mediterranean and Near Eastern roots, with relatively little evidence of western European ancestry. Instead, a PCA plot of the forty-eight individuals from this period suggested that they largely overlap with modern eastern Mediterranean and Near Eastern populations such as Greeks, Maltese, Cypriots and Syrians. Only two of the individuals showed continuity with the earlier Iron Age population of the region and others plotted to the Near East and North Africa. A similar shift to individuals with central or eastern Mediterranean ancestry in the imperial period also appeared in the Iberian Peninsula.[2] In Late Antiquity, however, the eastern Mediterranean component of the average ancestry of the city's inhabitants began to disappear in favour of more modern central European populations.

In 2024, Antonio et al. returned to the question of long-term continuity with a study of whole genomes from 240 individuals from Europe and the Mediterranean dating from *c.* 1000 BCE to *c.* 700 CE. Overall, the study found remarkable local genetic heterogeneity, particularly in Armenia and the city of Rome. However, this heterogeneity remained essentially stable into the present day, with estimates of between 7 and 11 per cent long-range migration. They hypothesize that during the Roman Empire, rapidly growing cities and military complexes drew a transient migratory population. However, the collapse of the empire may have eliminated incentives for such mobile populations to remain in what were, in a post-Roman world, remote areas.[3] Unfortunately, since the archaeological contexts of the samples used in both studies were not incorporated into these longitudinal investigations, one can only speculate on the extent to which social status and other factors might have correlated with movement, or whether the pronounced eastern Mediterranean character of the samples from the area of Rome represents a slave and former slave population or individuals of higher social status.

Well before the revolution in ancient DNA analysis brought about by next generation sequencing, the effects of what are traditionally called the Anglo-Saxon invasions of Britain have drawn geneticists' attention. Some historians and archaeologists have minimized migration from the Continent to explain the transformation of post-Roman Britain, while others have argued for massive population replacement. Attempts to add genomic data to the debate largely depended, as we have seen above, on modern DNA.[4] However, in 2016 Stephan Schiffels et al. published and analysed the whole ancient genomes from ten individuals in Cambridge dating to the late Iron Age, four from between the fifth and sixth centuries, and three from the seventh to ninth centuries.[5] They compared the allele frequencies of rare variants in a reference panel of 433 European individuals from Finland, Spain, Italy, the Netherlands and Denmark. The fifth- to sixth-century samples, although interred in similar burials, proved diverse, with one similar to the Iron Age samples, one more similar to the seventh- to ninth-century samples, and one showing a mixed ancestry. The later samples, by contrast, shared more rare variants with the Dutch than with the Iron Age samples. While admitting that the sample size was too small to make definitive conclusions about possible migratory processes, they concluded that early medieval migration took a variety of forms, including perhaps continued migration until at least into the ninth century and that new arrivals integrated with the indigenous population in a variety of different ways, producing ultimately a genetically mixed community that could nevertheless be culturally homogeneous.[6]

A subsequent study by Joscha Gretzinger, Schiffels and others greatly expanded on this earlier paper, focusing on genome-wide analysis of 460 medieval northwestern Europeans, including 278 from England.[7] The genomic analysis was accompanied by detailed archaeological data and found a substantial increase of continental northern European ancestry in early medieval England, reaching as high as 76 per cent in eastern England, although their study showed considerable regional variation. The similarities were greatest with modern Germans and Danes, which they concluded indicated not simply an elite migration, as some historians had suggested, but a substantial migration across the North Sea. Moreover, this was a migration not only of men but of women and men. The level of integration of migrants and locals varied considerably by location, although generally they found no difference in male burial practices and only slight difference in female burials. 'Integration,' they conclude, 'was probably dependent on the fortunes of specific families and their individual members.'

Scandinavia has likewise drawn considerable interest from geneticists looking to understand population changes at the end of Antiquity. A team led by Eske Willerslev published a paper in *Nature* that analysed the genomes of 442 individuals from across Europe to Greenland in order to explore the impact of Viking expansion.[8] The results of their investigation largely coincided with what is known from archaeological and historical records, namely that during the Viking age (roughly *c.* 750 to 1050 CE), the spread of Scandinavian-type ancestry to the east largely involved individuals with Swedish-like ancestry, while Norwegian-like ancestry predominated in Iceland, Greenland, Ireland and the Isle of Man. Danish-like ancestry predominates in England, although their analyses could not distinguish Viking-age migration from earlier continental migration in the fifth and sixth centuries. At the same time, they noted migration from the Baltic into modern Sweden and migration from the British Isles into western Scandinavia, as well as southern European ancestry in modern Denmark.

In 2023, a Swedish research team further refined the image of population transformation in Scandinavia during the Viking age with an emphasis on the internal transformation of the region. They published a 2,000-year genetic transect through Scandinavia beginning in the Iron Age based on a total of 297 ancient genomes and 16,638 modern individuals.[9] Crucial in the genomic history of the region was the Viking age, when the long-established pattern of genetic ancestry underwent a significant change. They found that a long-established north–south line divided Scandinavian population from at least this period.

Moreover, this period saw significant gene flow both from the British–Irish Isles and from the eastern Baltic. This was primarily the result of women brought into the region, although they also found some evidence of genetic contribution from British–Irish males during the period. The British–Irish contribution to Scandinavian ancestry has continued into the present, while the eastern Baltic ancestry has declined over time.

In addition to macro- or regional-scale studies, teams of geneticists are beginning to work with archaeologists and historians to provide a more comprehensive and tightly focused understanding of community formation and change at the end of Antiquity, particularly in southern Germany.

In 2018, Veeramah et al. published a study of thirty-six adult individuals from six Bavarian cemeteries located within what had been the former Roman Empire *c.* 500 that demonstrated signific long-distance female mobility into this region.[10] A PCA plot of these individuals found considerable variation with these sites, but with a marked sex bias. All of the men and thirteen of the women clustered among modern northern and central European individuals. However, nine of the women sampled showed clear signs of artificial skull deformation, a condition created by binding the heads of very young children. During Late Antiquity, this practice was most closely associated with the Huns and more eastern societies. All nine of these women were outliers on the PCA plot and were more similar to modern south-eastern Europeans while one had a profile similar to central Asian populations. However, even though these women would have been clearly distinguishable physically from other women in their communities, the assemblages of grave goods reflected local customs. This study demonstrated that long-distance migration of women suggests that local communities may have practised exogamy to form strategic alliances with powerful communities to the east.

More recently, a pre-print in *BioRxiv* by Jens Blöcher et al. returned to this same area and analysed 248 genomes from late-Roman and early medieval sites in southern Germany.[11] The study focused on a region that formed the frontier of the Roman Empire, and the careful genomic, isotopic and archaeological analysis showed how the region changed as the Empire dissolved. Already in the fifth century, the population showed a wide spectrum of ancestry from northern as well as southern Europe and beyond. However, culturally, even those with a pronounced northern genetic background were already practising Roman burial traditions. A major demographic shift occurred in the sixth century, when communities of predominantly northern European origin integrated with the population of the former Roman settlements. These individuals shared significant IBD connections with geographically distant contemporaneous individuals from Germany and England, as well as from Austria, Hungary, Croatia and Serbia, suggesting that individuals with a northern European ancestry across this vast area descended from populations that had lived far north of the Roman frontier in earlier centuries. However, much of the migration from the north probably took place prior to the period normally regarded as the 'Migration Period'. The movements that characterized the sixth century were more likely to have been short-distance movements within the region. In these new communities, incoming and local groups rapidly intermingled and organized around small biologically-related kinship groups which were predominantly patrilineal or bilateral.

This study is exemplary from a number of perspectives. It avoids attaching ethnic labels to any of the individuals or genetic groups that it studies; it seamlessly integrates genomic, isotopic, archaeological and textual evidence; and, by focusing on the comprehensive analysis of sites, it was able to uncover the diversity of these communities, even while recognizing significant changes during the sixth century. Finally, it offers an alternative understanding of mobility to the traditional image of barbarian migrations beginning in the fifth century, suggesting instead that migration from north to south had already been a constant and that the changes of the sixth century could best be understood by local mobility.

The Carpathian Basin as laboratory

Beginning in 2019, HistoGenes, an international, interdisciplinary project sponsored by the European Research Council through its Horizon 2020 programme, has been applying all of the tools discussed above to understand population changes, mobilities and structures in the Carpathian Basin and adjoining areas between *c.* 400 and 900 CE.[12] The project, directed by the geneticist Johannes Krause, the historian Walter Pohl, the archaeologist Tivadar Vida and myself, uses an approach similar to that seen in both the transect studies described above and especially the comprehensive, site-focused multidisciplinary approach seen in the Blöcher et al. paper. The scale of the project surpasses other regionally focused genetic projects by a considerable measure: thus far, it includes either the whole genomes or arrays of roughly 1240k SNPs from over 6,500 men, women and children. Whenever possible, rather than sampling, it has endeavoured to analyse all of the burials in dozens of cemeteries across the Carpathian Basin and adjoining areas. Moreover, these genetic sequences are accompanied by isotopic, anthropological, historical and archaeological analyses to produce a multidimensional image of the populations that lived in and around the middle

Danubian region. Small teams of historians, archaeologists, anthropologists and geneticists have produced a series of case studies focusing on sub-regions of the Carpathian Basin. At the same time, the entire team has met virtually every two weeks through the years to educate each other about their respective disciplines, discuss best practice and share progress on their individual projects.

As a result, its members have been able to explore changes in population across this region through the centuries at both the local and regional level. Its results, however preliminary, thus provide not only insight into the transformation of a crucial frontier region at the end of the Roman world, but also a case study of how, when properly applied and integrated with other disciplinary traditions, genomic data can transform our understanding of the transition from the Roman Empire to the kingdoms of the Middle Ages. It is with a brief presentation of some of the results of this unique project that we will conclude this volume.

Few parts of Europe witnessed so many population shifts in a few centuries as the Carpathian Basin, essentially Pannonia and adjacent regions, in this formative period between the disintegration of the Roman Empire in the west and the emergence of the medieval polities and societies that would characterize the region for centuries.

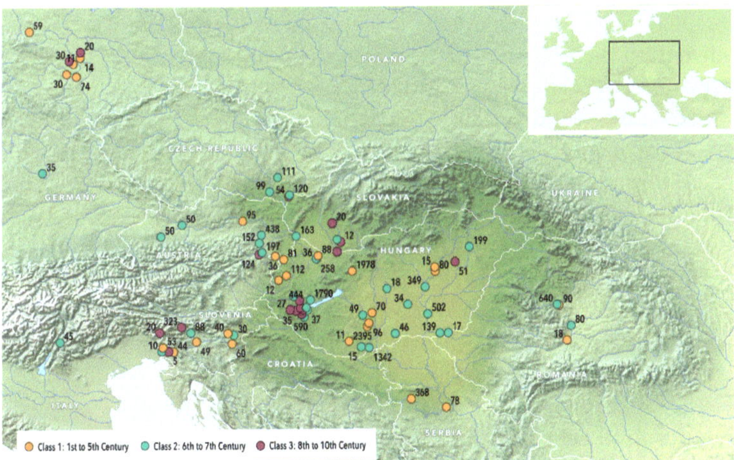

FIGURE 20 *Map of the region investigated by HistoGenes. Reproduced with permission of Michelle O'Reilly.*

Written sources record that Pannonians, Romans, Huns, Goths, Gepids, Langobards, Avars, Bulgars, Slavs, Franks and many other peoples settled or moved through this macro-region along the middle Danube. Since all written evidence about these momentous changes was produced outside of the region itself by Latin- or Greek-writing authors who lacked first-hand knowledge of life in post-Roman Pannonia, archaeological, anthropological and genomic evidence are essential to understand such questions and the impact of migrations and mobility in the region; the fate of the late-antique population as it disappeared or merged with new arrivals; the extent to which ethnonyms found in written sources corresponded with deeper social and cultural traditions; how health and diet affected these societies; and how local communities organized themselves, related to other, neighbouring communities and to wider networks of power and society.

Pannonia to the sixth century

By the sixth century, the population of what is today eastern Austria, Hungary, Slovakia, Czechia, Romania, Serbia and Slovenia was already a complex mixture. Inhabitants included Romanized indigenous Celtic and Illyrian populations, descendants of Roman legionaries and merchants, and members of various Germanic and Sarmatian peoples that had entered the Danubian region over the previous five centuries. Roman cities, fortifications and villas as well as indigenous peasant villages had likewise undergone complex changes through centuries of migration, conquest and warfare. The genetic composition of burials found in sixth-century sites traditionally identified as part of Langobard culture, therefore, must be situated within a much longer and wider history of population change in what was loosely termed Pannonia.[13]

Prior to the arrival of invading Romans *c.* 35 BCE, the Celtic and Illyrian populations of the lands along the Danube that would become Pannonia hardly regarded the region as a natural unity. Celtic populations had entered the middle and upper Danubian regions in the late fifth and early fourth centuries BCE. Early Celtic settlement sites formed part of what is generally known as La Tène civilization and spread from west to east along the Danube and its tributaries. Roman and Greek sources recorded the names of various Celtic kingdoms and peoples, but little can be known of their social or political organization, which seems to have been a series of loose confederations and transient polities. By the third century BCE, Celts had expanded into modern Transylvania, into territories well south of the Danube, into north-eastern Hungary and into the Great Hungarian Plain. Roman sources name a bewildering variety of Celtic peoples in the region, from the *Norici* in the upper reaches of the Drau and the *Boii* in what is today north-eastern Austria, to the *Scordisci* who settled in the Drava–Sava region around modern Belgrade.

To the south of these Celtic territories, the Illyrians had long controlled a series of petty kingdoms in the Balkans between the Adriatic and the Danube. A portion of this Illyrian population, the Pannonians, living south of the Danube, gave its name to the region, although Roman and Greek authors, ever since an expanding Roman Empire first entered a series of wars in the third century BCE, referred to the entire region simply as Illyricum.

Border clashes between Pannonians and *Norici* around 14 BCE provided a pretext for Rome to undertake a thorough conquest of the entire region, and by 9 BCE it had succeeded in eliminating significant opposition and incorporated all of the territories south of the Danube into the province of Illyria. The region remained volatile, however, and in 7 CE Illyrians, Dalmatians and Pannonians revolted against Roman rule. Emperor Tiberius (14–37 CE) crushed the revolt and dissolved Illyria into separate provinces. From the early first century, the area that lay between roughly the modern cities of Vienna and Sremska (Mitrovica) formed the province of Pannonia. Although at times divided administratively into two or even four provinces, the region formed for centuries a kind of frontier unity. This unity was reflected in the fourth-century creation of the Diocese of Pannonia, which included all of original Pannonia as well as the areas further up the Danube known as *Noricum Mediterraneum* and *Noricum Ripense* and downstream into Dalmatia between the Danube and the Adriatic.[14]

The integration of Pannonia into the Empire brought about major material, social and cultural transformations in the region.[15] For the conquering Romans, the main concern was the defence of the new frontier along the Danube. Thus, they started to erect a series of forts and watchtowers along the river.[16] These began as legionary encampments, but at important crossing points and at the confluence of tributaries into the Danube these encampments evolved into a series of permanent forts, around which grew up civilian communities. The primary military headquarters was established at Carnuntum, and a civilian settlement adjacent to the military centre developed into a city of some 50,000 inhabitants, the capital of Upper Pannonia (*Pannonia Superior*) and home port of the Danubian fleet as well as a strategic point on the Roman road system. Other military posts along the Danube, such as Vindobona (Vienna) and Brigetio (Komárom), grew into significant towns with civilian populations. So too did Savaria (Szombathely) on the ancient amber route connecting the Baltic with the Mediterranean; Scarbantia (Sopron) on the Neusiedler See/Fertő tó; Neviodunum (Drnovo) on the Sava; Siscia (Sisak) at the confluence of the Kupa, Sava and Odra rivers; Arrabona (Győr); Aquincum (Óbuda, Budapest); and Sirmium (Sremska Mitrovica), which became the capital of Lower Pannonia (*Pannonia inferior*).

The land immediately along the banks of the Danube continued under direct military control. Further back, behind this military zone, Rome established *coloniae*, settlements for veterans, which likewise grew in time into towns populated by former legionaries as well as new arrivals from Italy and nearby provinces. Outside of the towns proper, Roman surveyors parcelled out land that was distributed to veterans who proceeded to create villas, which were large agricultural exploitations of between two to four square kilometres. Archaeologists have identified some 600 villas across Roman Pannonia. Typically, at their centres were walled building complexes consisting of dwellings, some quite luxurious with mosaic floors, baths and hypocaust heating systems. They also included granaries, workshops for pottery and iron production and wineries.[17]

The surviving elements of the indigenous local population seem to have continued to live on more marginal land in small rural settlements, often located in areas where Romans had not established their villas. In such places, building practices continued pre-Roman forms, including partially sunken houses of wattle and daub or adobe constructions supported by four or six posts and roofed by thatch. Some of these settlements were inhabited continuously from pre-Roman into Roman times, such as Ménfőcsank, where a village of fifty-seven houses has been excavated.[18] At these sites, too, traditional forms of pottery and structures continued the Illyrian and Celtic traditions of the past. However, into the second and early third centuries CE, Roman building and craft traditions began to appear in some of these sites, indicating the gradual acculturation of the indigenous population by the Roman presence.

In contrast to the upper Rhine, which was peaceful and prosperous in the first centuries of Roman rule, the Pannonian frontier remained an active pressure point on the Empire. Across the Danube, various Germanic and Sarmatian polities repeatedly tested Roman defences, with the result that the Empire regularly stationed up to five legions along the river, frequently with three at Carnuntum and one at Sirmium.

This threat of trans-Danubian invasion became actual in 166 CE when an alliance of various barbarian groups overran the region between Vindobona and Carnuntum, pressed the *limes* up river in Noricum, and raided deep into Roman territory. These incursions were only being turned back by the philosopher Emperor Marcus Aurelius (161–80) shortly before they had reached Aquileia on the Adriatic. Although the Romans had no way of knowing it at the time, the composite armies under the collective name of *Marcomanni* or 'people of the borders' drew on groups from far beyond the border region. Archaeological evidence of Roman spoils taken during the fourteen-year war has been found deep in the northern areas of Germania and symptomized a major, if poorly understood, transformation of the barbarian world to the east of the Rhine and north of the Danube.

In the wake of the war, new peoples emerged and names of old peoples familiar to the Romans appeared in new places. For example, according to the Roman historian Cassius Dio, the first to attack the Roman frontier posts were six thousand *Langobardi* and *Obii* who had crossed the Danube near the Roman garrison of Brigetio. First-century Roman authors had placed the Langobards on the lower Elbe, over 1,000 kilometres away. If there were indeed Langobards in this raid, they were far from home. The Romans defeated these initial attacks, and after this incursion, the king of the *Marcomanni*, accompanied by ten ambassadors from the various peoples allied with him, sued for peace. The peace they concluded did not last, and soon the whole Rhine–Danube region became a battlefield. Although by his death in 180 Marcus Aurelius had succeeded in crushing the barbarian coalitions and driving them back across the Danube, and even planned to establish new provinces north of the river, his son and successor Commodus (177–92) abandoned the idea. Commodus focused instead on defending the Danubian frontier and rebuilding the Pannonian region that had been devastated by years of warfare.

The century following the end of the Marcomannic Wars was a period of crisis and disruption throughout much of the Roman Empire. Commodus was decidedly unequal to the task of succeeding his father and was ultimately assassinated. What followed was unprecedented turmoil across the Empire. Germanic raids across the Rhine and Danubian frontiers disrupted the Western Empire, while wars with Sassanid Persia threatened the eastern borders, defeating and capturing the Emperor Valerian (253–60) at Edessa in 260. Amazigh tribes in North Africa raided into the rich agricultural areas of the Mediterranean littoral.

Initially, Pannonia actually benefited from the crisis of the third century. Septimus Severus (193–211), who emerged victorious in the bloody year of the five emperors, had commanded the legions stationed along the Danube at the time of Commodus' assassination, and his troops had raised him to the imperial dignity at Carnuntum. After consolidating his power, he channelled resources into Pannonia. The reasons for this were not sentimental: he was absolutely dependent on the support of his Pannonian legions. Moreover, the increased threats to the Danubian frontier made this peripheral area of the Empire central to the protection of Italy and Rome. Under Severus and his immediate successors, massive investments in troops, fortifications and communication and supply networks introduced what has been termed the 'golden age of Pannonia', as security concerns brought more military presence and, with it, wealth and power. Of course, Pannonia too suffered during this period, particularly during devastating attacks between 258 and 260. However, archaeological evidence shows that Rome did not abandon the region but repeatedly restored devastated Pannonian towns in the late third and early fourth centuries.

Throughout the crisis, the Danubian provinces of Raetia, Pannonia and Moesia were major recruiting grounds for the imperial armies, armies that raised their commanders to the imperial dignity, or at least attempted to do so. The region had never been a centre for the production of wealth through agriculture or manufacture, but the influx of silver, in the form of military pay, resulted in a booming regional economy. Emperors of the later third and fourth centuries were, with few exceptions, provincial soldiers from the Danubian region who had risen through the ranks, not members of traditional senatorial elites,[19] and they did not forget their homeland as they rose to the purple.

Pannonia's *Romanitas*, however, was of a peculiar sort. Few members of the traditional Roman elite made Pannonia their homes. Apart from merchants along the amber road, the region had few permanent settlers from Italy. Its population was largely active-duty soldiers and descendants of the mixture of retired veterans and local Celts and Illyrians who contributed their sons to the army. As the Roman army became increasingly dependent on semi-Romanized provincial populations and barbarians for recruitment, the distinction between Roman and barbarian became increasingly tenuous, with Roman armies largely manned with troops from federated barbarian allies. Moreover, after the division of the Empire into eastern and western halves in the fourth century, Pannonia and Illyria, while still important sources of troops, were increasingly marginal to the geo-strategic concerns of the Empire itself, which concentrated increasingly on the eastern frontiers with Sassanid Persia and separatist movements in the west.

Under these circumstances, the long Danubian frontier became increasingly difficult to defend. In the lower Danube, the Gothic confederation raided into the Empire. Further up river, Sarmatians, Quadi, Vandals and Marcomanni continued to press frontier posts. The civilian society suffered enormously: once-prosperous towns were almost deserted, and commerce along the amber route virtually ended. When Emperor Valentinian I (364–75), himself a native of Pannonia, began to establish fortifications on the right bank of the Danube in Quadi territory to prevent such incursions, the Quadi revolted, forcing the Emperor to hurry to Carnuntum, which he found ruined and virtually deserted, and then to Aquincum, from which he launched a punitive trans-Danubian campaign. The Quadi sued for peace, but, according to the historian Ammianus Marcellinus, Valentinian became so furious with the Quadi emissaries who came to negotiate that he suffered a stroke and died.

The Huns: a migration that wasn't

Shortly thereafter, however, the arrival of the Huns from central Asia in the region of the lower Danube and Black Sea changed everything throughout Illyria and Pannonia. The Huns defeated the Gothic confederation, already weakened by punitive wars against them launched by Valentinian's younger brother and successor, Valens (364–78). When a portion of the Goths, the *Thervingi*, were permitted entry into the Empire, Roman mismanagement pushed them into revolt and in a catastrophic battle fought in 378 near the city of Adrianople (Edirne), Valens was killed and his army destroyed. While the Goths failed to reach Constantinople, they raided deeply throughout Pannonia and Illyria before coming to terms with the Emperor Theodosius I (379–95), who allowed them to settle on the lower Danube in Thrace with their own autonomous political and military systems intact.[20]

Into the early fifth century, Pannonia was repeatedly the victim of raids by Goths, Sarmatians, Quadi, Alans, Huns, Vandals and Marcomanni, while Roman resistance and indeed presence became increasingly tenuous. Roman elites and the military units that had defended the region withdrew, leaving the civilian Romanized population to develop a *modus vivendi* with the barbarian groups across the Danube. Romans progressively abandoned the villas and small towns of the earlier periods, and the remnants of the Romanized population withdrew into the confines of remaining fortified sites such as Gorsium, Aarrabona, Scarbantia and Aquincum. However, even in these sites, archaeological evidence suggests that their populations were a mixture of Roman provincials and barbarians.[21]

Roman control ended entirely in the first third of the fifth century, when the expanding Hunnic confederation seized control of the region, a *de facto* situation that was probably officially recognized around 433 by the West Roman commander Aetius (391–454), who used his close relationship with the Huns in his own political machinations within the Empire. Hunnic lordship brought a semblance of peace to the region, even while the Huns brought widespread devastation to surrounding imperial provinces. Especially during the reign of Attila (434–53), the various regional populations, including Goths, Pannonians, Gepids, Rugii, Sciri, Eruli, Suebi and Sarmatians, were subordinated to Hunnic power and their warriors incorporated into the Hunnic military forces that threatened both the eastern and western Empires and participated in Hunnic wars in Gaul and Italy.

Our ongoing studies of fifth-century sites do not support evidence of a significant migration of central Asians into Pannonia during the Hunnic period. There is evidence of some cultural practices associated with Steppe societies, as well as evidence of some central Asian genetic continuity, but both are diffuse and limited. For example, of the fifteen individuals we examined at Fonyód in western Hungary, which dates from the period of Hunnic control of the region in the middle of the fifth century, seven showed evidence of artificial cranial deformation, a cultural practice more common in Eastern societies. However, most of the population showed either a northern or southern European heritage, although two individuals carried a south or south-eastern Asian ancestry, perhaps indicative of some connections to the East.[22]

A recent, comprehensive study of 369 individuals from the period of Hunnic occupation reinforces the impression that the Hunnic conquest was not accompanied by a significant migration of central Asians.[23] We found no evidence of a significant population movement from the eastern and central Steppes of Asia into the Carpathian Basin during the fifth century. Instead, we found a pronounced heterogeneity within the population, including those whose burial context suggests an eastern Steppe tradition. Only 6 per cent of the individuals showed a north-east Asian or Steppe admixture. Nor did the study find a strong correlation between genetic ancestry and either artificial cranial deformation or the presence of objects that suggest a Steppe origin. While scattered finds, particularly in solitary or small grave groups, show genetic continuity with Asia and even some distant connections with inhabitants of the Xiongnu Empire, which had disappeared at the end of the first century CE, these are minor elements in the complex picture of the fifth century. Figure 21 shows the IBD connections between the Carpathian region and what had been the Xiongnu Empire. Clearly, while such distant connections existed, they did not indicate a massive population movement from east to west.

We can conclude that while there were certainly some high-status individuals within the Hunnic realm whose complex ancestry included some ancestors among Xiongnu, the Huns who so terrorized the Byzantine and Western Empires in the fourth and fifth centuries were, as written sources suggested, a heterogeneous

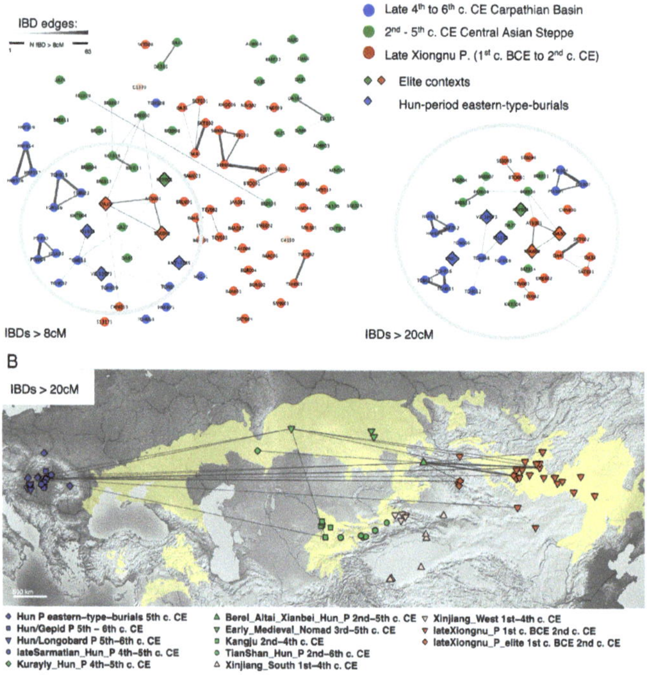

FIGURE 21 *IBD connections between Hunnic-period individuals. Gnecchi-Ruscone et al., 'Ancient Genomes Reveal Trans-Eurasian Connections between the European Huns and the Xiongnu Empire', fig. 4. Available under a CC BY 4.0 license.*

people whose genetic background stretched from Asia to Europe. Their historical impact and the dislocation and destruction that they brought about were not proportionate to their demographic impact, which was minimal at best.

In any case, their influence in the region was short-lived. Internal warfare erupted once more after Attila's death in 453 when a coalition of subordinated peoples rebelled against Hunnic rule. After the Hunnic defeat on the Nedao River the following year, the primary victors were the Gepids, who took over the core of the former Hunnic kingdom, around the River Tisza, east from the Danube, while a Rugian kingdom arose in the west, a Herulian kingdom north of the Danube into modern Moravia, and smaller

Suebian, Scirian and Sarmatian groups in the Hungarian plain. Western Roman Emperor Avitus (455–6) took advantage of the situation to reconquer much of Pannonia, but he soon ceded the area between Sirmium and Vindobona to the Ostrogothic King Valamir (*c.* 420–69), with the intention of using the Goths as a shield against the barbarians north of the Danube. Indeed, the Goths were able to defeat raids by the Suebi in 468 and a combined attack of Suebi, Regii, Skiri and Sarmatians the following year.

Gothic dominion probably extended in a crescent shape from Lake Balaton to the Drava and then down the Danube to Sirmium,[24] but archaeological evidence of Gothic settlement as well as any hint of a genetic influence on the region's population are virtually non-existent. Their actual presence in the region must have been very slight, ruling through local proxies, although they seem to have occasionally reused buildings in some of the surviving Roman towns. At Keszthely in particular, the Ostrogoths may have reused Roman fortifications at Fenékpuszta and the Christian basilica, although it may not have had a religious function.[25] Since the Goths, and indeed the barbarian kingdoms north of the Danube, had entered into treaties with Rome, the Empire could claim that it had once more regained Pannonia, although in reality Roman political and military authority in the region had disappeared. Moreover, in 473 the Gothic army abandoned Pannonia for Italy, leaving the local population largely at the mercy of the various petty kingdoms north of the Danube. The Gepids filled the vacuum to the east and south, reconquering Sirmium by 505. From the north, a new/old people, the Langobards, conquered the Rugii and then, sometime in the first quarter of the sixth century, occupied Pannonia south of the Danube up to the territory of the Gepids.

Populations in Pannonia at the end of Antiquity

The demographic effects of this turbulent history are evident in the complex genomic patterns observable in the region by the end of the fifth century. First, in contradiction to the assumption that before major migrations into the region, populations on either side of the Roman *limes* represented different populations, we see already a spectrum of genetic ancestries similar to what has been found for the city of Rome itself. As we saw above, the 2019 Antonio et al. study that examined the changing genomic profile of the city of Rome across the past 12,000 years found that, during the height of the Empire, the city's population showed a strong Mediterranean and Near Eastern profile, a profile that changed with the Empire's decline.[26] The twenty-four individuals sampled showed a shift away from the Near East toward the west and north, paralleling perhaps the split of the Empire itself into eastern and western components.

In our own investigations in what is today Austria, Hungary and Slovenia, we are finding a similar, broad population in the imperial period in these provincial areas that is quite similar to that of Rome itself, with individuals whose background points to the Near East and to Africa. In modern Slovenia, for example, cemeteries from the Roman period show a population with a preponderance of European backgrounds, but outliers that point to North Africa as well as the Near East. This begins to change dramatically in the post-Roman period, with North Africa and Near East components disappearing. Instead, the population, as in Rome itself, began to more closely resemble that of later Italy.

While the African and Near Eastern profile disappears with the end of Antiquity, we continue to find on both sides of the *limes*, populations whose ancestry is already composed of elements that would plot from Scandinavia to the Italian peninsula. We find the same complexity in the Lake Balaton region in modern Hungary, even before the recorded migrations of Germanic populations. A study of four sites on the southern shore of the Balaton show that, while eastern Mediterranean and North African ancestry does not appear, already in the fifth century the diversity in the small region mirrors all of western and southern Europe. When plotted against a genetic map of Europe, we find ancestries that reach across Europe from north to south.[27] Figure 22 shows that when the populations of these four cemeteries are projected onto a PCA of Europe, individuals' ancestries range from Scandinavia to Italy.

What is perhaps yet more extraordinary is that even beyond the frontiers of the Roman Empire, we find the same mixture of individuals with both the northern and southern genomic profiles. Clearly, even while 'barbarians' filtered into the Empire for centuries, some southerners found a place into Germanic societies. In fourth- and fifth-century sites studied in what is now north-western Hungary, we see a population that is primarily composed of individuals with

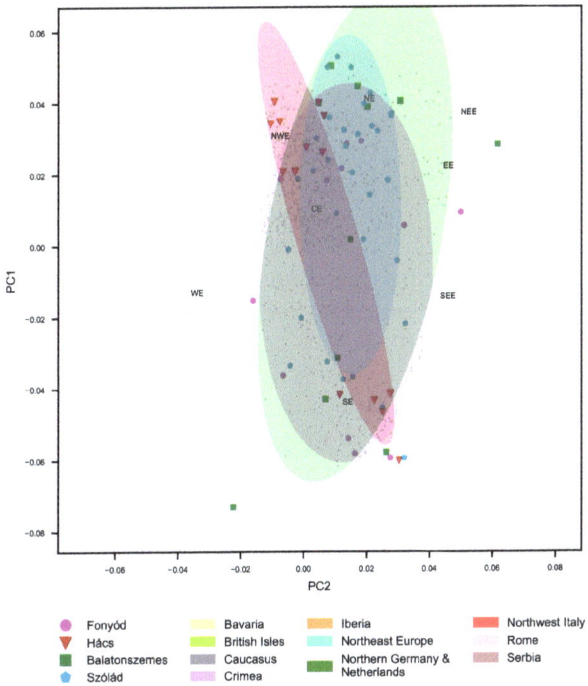

FIGURE 22 *PCA plots of four cemeteries south of Lake Balaton. Vyas et al., 'Fine-Scale Sampling Uncovers the Complexity of Migrations in 5th–6th Century Pannonia', fig. 2A. Available under a CC BY 4.0 license.*

southern European ancestry, but in addition a good number show a mixture of northern and southern European and even a few individuals with some sub-Saharan, Iberian and Asian ancestry.

We find the same complexity along the Roman *limes* from the Vienna woods that compares with the profile seen in distant Slovenia at the same time. Such findings, consistent with those found by Jens Blöcher in southern Germany,[28] clearly suggest that the presence of Roman colonists, and perhaps even more significantly Roman military, brought individuals from across the Empire into this important border region while at the same time groups from beyond the *limes* were already settling within imperial territories.

At the end of Antiquity, Asian and African ancestry disappears in these frontier areas just as it does in Rome itself and we see a much greater influx from northern Europe. In Szeleste on the Little Hungarian Plain in north-western Hungary, for example, we see a preponderance of individuals with a northern European ancestry as well as the continued presence of those of a southern background and already considerable merging of the two.[29]

It is hardly surprising that along the Danubian frontier, individuals with what would have been seen as a barbarian heritage filter into and ultimately begin to outnumber those with a southern ancestry. What is perhaps even more extraordinary is that even beyond the Roman frontiers of the Roman Empire, we find the same mixture of individuals with both the northern and southern genomic profiles. In the Elbe–Saale region of eastern Germany, recent genomic analysis, as seen in Figure 23, reveals the presence of numerous individuals with a genetic background that points to southern Europe and the Roman world.[30]

Why these individuals with a southern ancestry are found so far into the Germanic world is not yet known. They may have been merchants or the descendants of women and children captured in raids, but if so, they appear to have been thoroughly integrated into

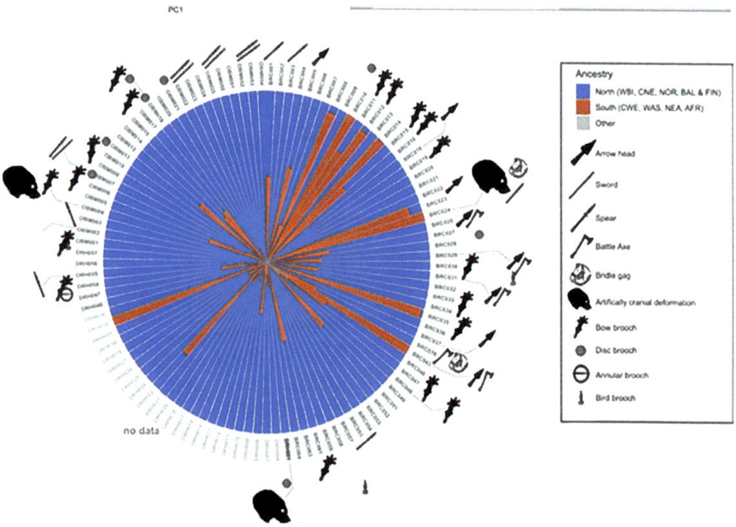

FIGURE 23 *Late antique populations in eastern Germany. Gretzinger et al., 'Ancient DNA Connects Large-Scale Migration with the Spread of Slavs', Extended data fig. 3. Available under a CC BY 4.0 license.*

the local societies. As one sees in Figure 23, their grave goods and burials are indistinguishable from those with a more typically northern background. Perhaps some were merchants or even economic emigrants. Clearly, even while 'barbarians' filtered into the Empire for centuries, some southerners found a place in Germanic societies. In terms of population and ancestry, both sides of the *limes* resembled each other even before the arrival of groups such as the Langobards.

The Langobards: migration or intensification?

The Langobards first appear in Roman texts early in the first century of the Common Era (CE), when the Roman historian Velleius Paterculus, writing about the military expedition of Tiberius around 10 CE in which he himself participated, listed among the peoples defeated by the Romans the 'Langobards, a people surpassing even the Germans in savagery'.[31] The geographer Strabo, writing around the same time, considered the Langobards a part of the Suebi and stated that they were at present living on the eastern banks of the Elbe.[32] He described their lifestyle as essentially nomadic, saying that they lived for the most part from their flocks dwelling in temporary huts and packing all of their goods into wagons when moving. At the end of the first century, the Roman historian Cornelius Tacitus, in his *Annales*, briefly describes the Langobards along with the Semnones as among those who revolted against the Romanized Suebian King Maroboduus around 17 CE.[33] In his *Germania*, written around 98, his only mention of the Langobards is the terse comment that they are distinguished by their small numbers and find safety only in battle.[34] After this the Langobards disappear from Roman texts; until, as we have seen, the beginning of the Marcomannic Wars. It was then, according to Cassius Dio, writing in the early third century, that during the reign of Marcus Aurelius, 6,000 Langobards and Obii crossed the Danube but were soundly defeated, sued for peace and then returned home.[35]

The name of the Langobards only reappears some 300 years later in the writings of the Byzantine historian Procopius. Procopius describes these Langobards around 490 as a Christian people living across the Danube but under the domination of the Heruli, one of the groups that had profited from the collapse of the Hunnic confederation to occupy parts of modern Hungary and Moravia.[36]

Procopius further wrote that *c.* 508 the Langobards defeated the Heruli, killing their king, Rodulf, and driving out the rest of their former overlords. These territories south of the Danube were in the former Roman province of Pannonia, from which, as noted above, Roman administrative and military infrastructure had withdrawn in the course of the fifth century. Pannonia had fallen first under Hunnic, then under Ostrogothic control, when the Ostrogoths moved into the Balkans in 473. Soon after, in 476, Odoacer (*c.* 433–93), a Roman commander of barbarian origin in Italy who led a mixed army of Heruli, Rugii and others, overthrew the last West Roman emperor and ruled Italy as king and patricius by arrangement with the East Roman emperor in Constantinople. He exerted loose control over the former Roman provinces to the north and east, including Pannonia. The population of the region thus presumably comprised descendants of Roman provincials as well as members of the various barbarian populations that had entered the region over the previous two centuries.

In 493 the Ostrogothic king Theoderic the Great (454–526), acting on the orders of the Roman Emperor Zeno (*c.* 425–91), who had made him patrician and master of the military in the west, killed Odoacer and took over the Kingdom of Italy, which he ruled nominally as a representative of the emperor until his death in 526. Taking advantage of a troubled succession within the Ostrogothic kingdom, in 535 the Byzantine (East Roman) Empire invaded Italy and began a reconquest under Emperor Justinian I (*c.* 482–565). From around this time, Byzantine diplomacy began to develop treaties with the Langobards in order to isolate the Ostrogoths and to counter the Gepids, whose power had expanded along the Danube and Tisa Rivers, and granted them the 'city of Noricum and the fortifications in Pannonia as well as other towns and a great amount of money'.[37] This probably took place around the period 547–8, and legitimized the entry of the Langobards into the former Roman provinces south of the Danube that had already begun around 500 and had expanded south of Lake Balaton by the 530s or 540s. Thereafter the fortunes of the Langobards were progressively intertwined with those of the Romans: Romans sided with the Langobards in their increasingly serious conflicts with the Gepids, and the Langobards provided troops to aid the Romans against the Ostrogoths. After the death of Justinian in 565 and the succession of Justin II (*c.* 520–78), however, Roman policy shifted to support for the Gepids and in 566 the latter defeated the Langobards with Roman support. This drove the Langobards into an alliance with the central Asian Avars who had newly arrived in the Pannonia to the east of the Gepids.[38] This alliance made possible the Langobards' final defeat of the Gepid kingdom in 567 under the command of the Langobard King Alboin (*c.* 530–72).

The extent of a demographic impact caused by the Langobard occupation of Pannonia is difficult to assess, as is the hypothesis that the Langobards living on the Elbe in the first century were the same as those who appeared along the Danube in the fifth. The practice of cremation rather than inhumation until into the late fifth century makes it impossible to obtain extensive aDNA evidence from Scandinavia. A recent study by Hugh McColl et al. of 712 new ancient genomes shows IBD connections between southern Scandinavia and populations in what would become the Langobard kingdom along the Danube and, ultimately, in Italy.[39] True, a mid-sixth-century site at Lake Balaton indicates the presence of a pedigree with a northern European origin and enhanced status,[40] but this same genetic pool also appears in Britain, suggesting a more diffuse spread from southern Scandinavia both west and south. Moreover, as we have seen, Scandinavian ancestry was already widely present in central and southern Europe for centuries, and thus the Langobards of the late-fifth and sixth centuries need not be evidence of the arrival of a new, cohesive population directly from Scandinavia.

What we do see in at least one extensively studied site is that while the populations of a more northern background were already in the region, those populations differed among themselves. This is evident in Figure 24, which shows that while three fifth-century sites around the western Balaton all show individuals of northern ancestry, they do not coincide. However, in the mid-sixth-century site of Szólád, we see the presence of individuals who correspond with all three of these earlier groups. This may suggest that the Langobard movement into the region not only increased the percentage of individuals with a northern ancestry, but effected the political consolidation under which Langobard rule combined previously disparate groups.

The hypothesis that the Langobard rule brought about changes in the demographics of Pannonia is also suggested by the evidence

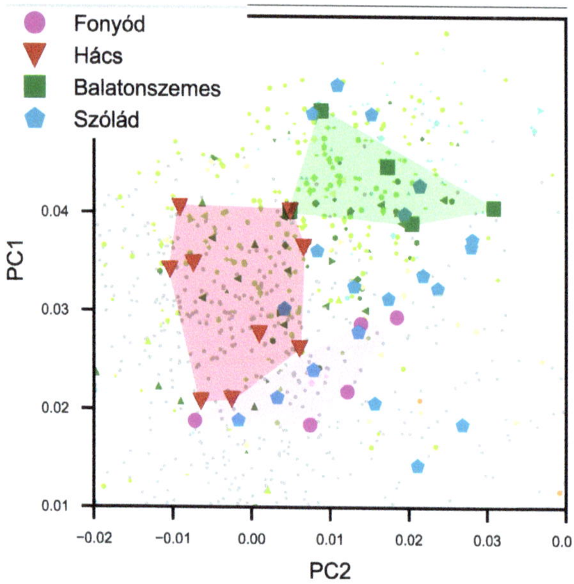

FIGURE 24 *PCA plot of four late-fifth- to sixth-century sites near Lake Balaton. Vyas et al., 'Fine-Scale Sampling Uncovers the Complexity of Migrations in 5th–6th Century Pannonia', fig. 3C. Available under a CC BY 4.0 license.*

of mobility to newly established communities. At Szólád, not only does one find a mixture of all of the various north-central genetic origins that had appeared earlier in the region, but that all of the adults were born elsewhere and migrated to this site south of Lake Balaton in adulthood. Nevertheless, although all were new arrivals, one can see a gender difference in their origins (see Figure 25).

The analysis of strontium is indicative of whether an individual was native or exotic to the place of burial.[41] At Szólád, the strontium signal of both men and women suggests that the adults who made up the community came from a wide catchment area and that men and women did not originate in the same locations. It may well be that under Langobard rule, new social and military units were formed from men of different backgrounds and that these in turn took wives from a wide area.

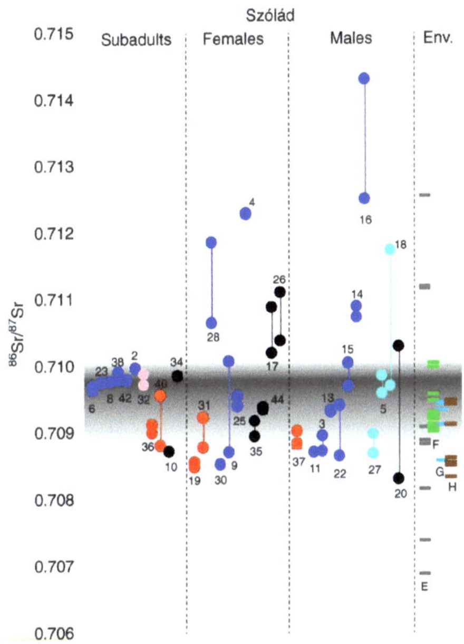

FIGURE 25 *Strontium isotope ratios at Szólád. Isotope data from Szólád are taken from Alt et al., 'Lombards on the Move – An Integrative Study of the Migration Period Cemetery at Szólád, Hungary'. Vertical lines indicate cases where multiple teeth were collected from the same individual. The gray band indicates the local bioavailable strontium isotope range. Individuals outside this range are considered non-local. Colour coding indicates predominantly northern (blue) or predominantly southern (red) ancestry. Samples shown in black are those with missing genomic data. Amorim et al., 'Understanding 6th-Century Barbarian Social Organization', fig. 5. Available under a CC BY 4.0 license.*

However, the organization of communities varied greatly in the sixth century. Our exhaustive analysis of individual cemeteries within discrete regions has made it possible for us also to examine the often-assumed relationship between ancestry and cultural tradition. Archaeologists have long argued that certain kinds of material culture represented in female dress or certain kinds of grave goods indicate adherence and belonging to specific cultural groups. While this may be true in some cases, we find communities with the same origin but different social and cultural practices, as well as nearby communities with the same material culture; for example, in the two nearby contemporary cemeteries of Hegykő and Szeleste in the Little Hungarian Plain, we find two contemporaneous communities with the same genetic profile. However, the size and structure of pedigrees, cemetery organization and isotope patterns differ significantly. At Hegykő, 67 per cent of all of the individuals were part of one of ten pedigrees, each consisting on average of 4.5 individuals. At Szeleste, only 34 per cent of individuals belonged to fourteen identified pedigrees, and these tended to be smaller than at Hegykő. Moreover, while at Hegykő, members of the same pedigree were buried closely together, at Szeleste only core families were buried together – more distant relatives were scattered across the cemetery. Finally, while at Hegykő we found a strong correlation between types and numbers of grave goods and genetic ancestry, no such correlation existed at Szeleste. Clearly these contemporaneous communities followed different social traditions in spite of similar genetic background.[42]

The Italian Langobard Kingdom

King Alboin did not use his victory to build a hegemonial kingdom along the Middle Danube (as the Avars would soon do in the next century), but rather to assemble a large army to invade Italy. Later sources date the beginning of this march to 1 April 568. Even though some historians have argued that it may also have happened in 569, we can be rather precise about the date, and historians even assume that their route followed the ancient Roman Via Postumia to Aquileia and Verona, even though no archaeological evidence survives for these events.[43] Seventh-century sources attribute the Langobard invasion of Italy in 568 to an invitation issued to the Langobard King Alboin by the Roman commander Narses, although this is not mentioned in sixth-century sources and is greeted with scepticism by modern scholars.[44] It was clear that the battered infrastructure in Pannonia could not meet the ambitions of a growing Langobard army, which now had also incorporated part of the defeated Gepids. Later sources claimed that Alboin had left his former kingdom to his Avar allies.[45] The invasion met with surprisingly little organized Roman resistance, but still the Langobard conquest of parts of Italy was a poorly organized and long-drawn-out affair. The main army moved westward and took Pavia, which would later become the Langobard capital, after a siege, but did not move on to attack Ravenna or Rome. Instead, Alboin's army began to fall apart into separate bands led by individual dukes who went their own ways, some into southern Italy and others into Burgundy, and some straight into Roman service. Alboin and his immediate successor were both assassinated. After a decade, facing conquest by Frankish armies, the Langobard dukes recognized the need to re-establish some central authority and elected Authari (*c.* 540–90) king in *c.* 584. Along with his Bavarian wife Theodelinda (*c.* 570–628), a descendant of an earlier Langobard king, Authari re-established royal rule. Upon Authari's death in 590, Theodelinda then married his successor, Agilulf (591–616), duke of Turin, but described by sources as a Thuringian. In spite of its consolidation, the Langobard kingdom only controlled the north of Italy with the exception of the modern Romagna around Ravenna, and Tuscany; the largely independent Langobard duchies of Spoleto and Benevento ruled much of the inland areas of the peninsula, while the coastal strips and the land around Ravenna and Rome remained under Roman control.

Under the patronage of Theodelinda, Secundus of Non/Trent, wrote a short history of the Langobards that has subsequently disappeared. During dynastic disputes in the second half of the seventh century, the *Origo Gentis Langobardorum*, a brief account of the mythic origins of the Langobards written within the context of rival dynastic interests, presented their origins in 'Scandanan', where they carried the name of the Winnili. Attacked by the Vandals, they obtained favour from Wodan through the intervention of his wife Frea, and acquired the name Langobards or long-beards. The text then tells of their migration through various regions before establishing themselves in the former land of the Rugii, where they fought with and defeated the Heruls and then came into conflict with the Gepids. The text details the various royal marriage alliances with Gepids, Thuringians, Franks and Heruls prior to the movement of the Langobards into Pannonia. It also tells of the final defeat of the Gepids in which King Alboin killed the Gepid King Cunimund, the king's marriage with the daughter of Cunimund, Rosemund, and the invasion of Italy. This text makes no mention of alliances with the Byzantines nor does it credit the invasion of Italy to an invitation from Narses.[46]

At the end of the eighth century, after the Langobard kingdom had been conquered by the Frankish King Charles the Great (Charlemagne, 742–814) in 774, the Langobard cleric Paul the Deacon wrote a much fuller history of the Langobards, drawing on the *Origo Gentis Langobardorum*, the now-lost history of Secundus, and other seventh-century sources. Paul's account, although written over two centuries or more after the events it recounts, has nevertheless been taken, often uncritically, as a reliable survey of Langobard history, a position increasingly disputed.[47] Paul the Deacon describes Alboin's invading army as a polyethnic force, consisting not only of Langobards but also Gepids, Bulgars, Sarmatians, Pannonians, Suevi, Noricans and others.[48]

Since the Langobards were illiterate prior to their entry into the Roman world and contemporary Roman authors had little interest in describing the Langobards except in military and political terms, the social structure of pre-migration Langobard society is extremely difficult to reconstruct. Much depends on whether one sees the seventh-century legal compilations, and in particular the Edict of King Rothari promulgated in 643, as containing some indication of pre-migration social and cultural organization.[49] If this text, written in Latin but containing many Langobard terms, reflects anything of pre-conquest Langobard society, then judging from the compensation tariffs attached to individuals, the society was divided into three strata: free-born (termed *exercitales* or soldiers in later laws), *aldii* or clients, and *servi*, slaves.[50] An important but poorly understood social institution was the *fara*. The contemporary Bishop Marius of Avenches, who penned a laconic chronicle of his times, describes the invasion of Italy as having taken place '*in fara*',[51] and the Edict of Rothari includes a provision for a free man to move about 'with his fara'.[52] A number of place names, both in Italy and in other regions such as Burgundy occupied by barbarian armies include the term *fara*, as do some personal names from Burgundy, although the interpretation of this evidence is uncertain. By the late eighth century, Paul the Deacon defined *fara* as a kin group.[53] However, recent scholarship has argued on etymological grounds that the term originally designated not a kindred but a small, mobile military unit, which only acquired the meaning of a kindred following the establishment of the Langobard Kingdom in Italy.[54]

Our research indeed shows strong genetic and cultural ties between the Pannonia of the mid-sixth century and northern Italy in the early seventh and has allowed us to trace the creation of new settlements in Italy following the Langobard conquest.

The Piedmontese village of Collegno shows identity by descent connections between individuals buried there and Szólád and Fonyód, with more distant connections through Szólád to individuals buried a century or so earlier at Balatonszemes and Hács.

An analysis of this Piedmont location also shows the manner in which newcomers entered and transformed the area. An analysis of fifty-two individuals buried in the early seventh-century cemetery of Collegno, combining archaeological, isotopic and genomic data, allowed us to recognize three distinct pedigrees within the community.[55] The earliest members of the community, buried in the centre of the cemetery around 600, are made up of three biologically related groups, CL1, CL2 and CL3 (see Figure 27), which ultimately coalesced into a single pedigree.

The first two groups were already closely related individuals with similar central-northern European ancestry. Their ancestry was quite distinct from that of other roughly contemporary burials in the region and suggests that they represent a change in the demographic make-up of the Piedmont. Their high social status is evident from the presence of elaborate belt sets and weapons for the

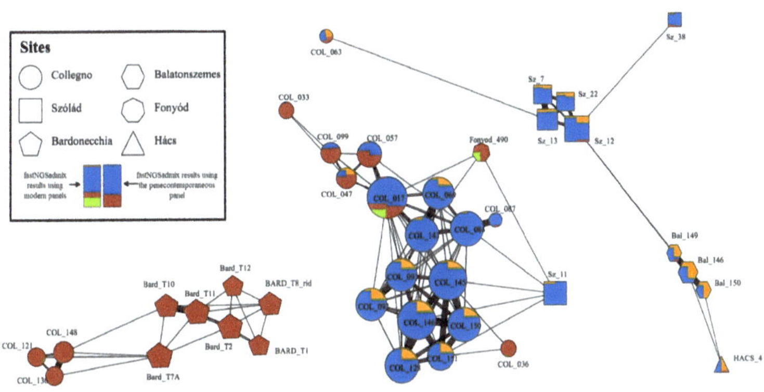

FIGURE 26 *IBD connections between Collegno, Italy and the Balaton areas. Tian et al., 'The Role of Emerging Elites in the Formation and Development of Communities after the Fall of the Roman Empire', fig. 4. Available under a CC BY 4.0 license.*

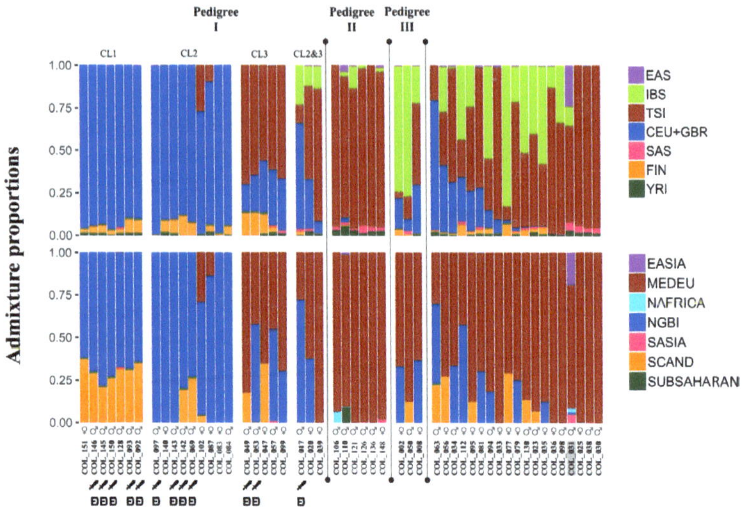

FIGURE 27 *Admixture plots of Collegno burials, with modern populations top and contemporary populations bottom. Tian et al., 'The Role of Emerging Elites in the Formation and Development of Communities after the Fall of the Roman Empire', fig. 2. Copyright © 2024 the Authors. Published by PNAS. This open access article is distributed under a CC BY 4.0 license.*

men, as well as complex grave structures. IBD connections between this pedigree and individuals from Pannonia as well as non-local strontium signals for the earliest of this pedigree suggest that this group may indeed have arrived in Collegno from elsewhere.

A third group – CL3 in the Admixture table above – that arrived early at the site and also showed evidence of elite status, such as gold folia crosses, weapons and elaborate goods, had a different ancestry: while mixed, it was predominantly southern European in origin. They also consumed a diet different from that of the first two groups. However, in the second generation a woman from the former group (CL2 in Figure 28) married a man from this third group, effectively combining the three into a single pedigree.

A second pedigree, composed of individuals with a marked southern ancestry, lacked the markers of high social status, but were nonetheless consistently buried near the members of the first

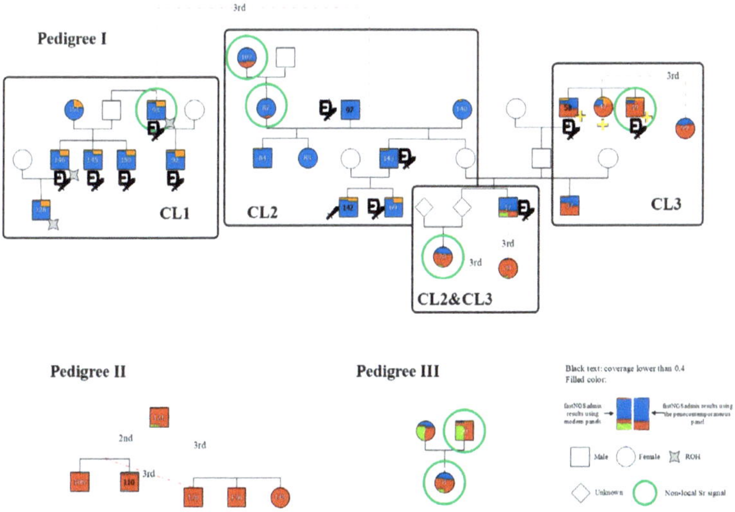

FIGURE 28 *Pedigrees at Collegno. Tian et al., 'The Role of Emerging Elites in the Formation and Development of Communities after the Fall of the Roman Empire', fig. 3E. Available under a CC BY 4.0 license.*

subgroup in Pedigree I, suggesting a strong bond between these groups.

At some point in the seventh century, a new, third population began to bury its dead in the Collegno cemetery. These individuals, as well as other non-related individuals, had a markedly different ancestry from those of pedigrees I and II that may have indicated a background to the southwest – possibly the Iberian Peninsula or southern Gaul – and practised a different form of burial in small, irregular-shaped pits without any artefacts. Carbon and nitrogen values indicate that they also had a diet different from that of the established members of the community.

Figure 29 shows that individuals of this newly arriving group maintained a diet distinct from that of the earlier pedigrees. Their diet consisted primarily of C_3 plants such as wheat, while those with a more northern ancestry and higher status to judge by their grave goods consumed more C_4 plants such as millet. Although living in the same community, these kin groups differed in their foodways as well as in their ancestry and social status.[56]

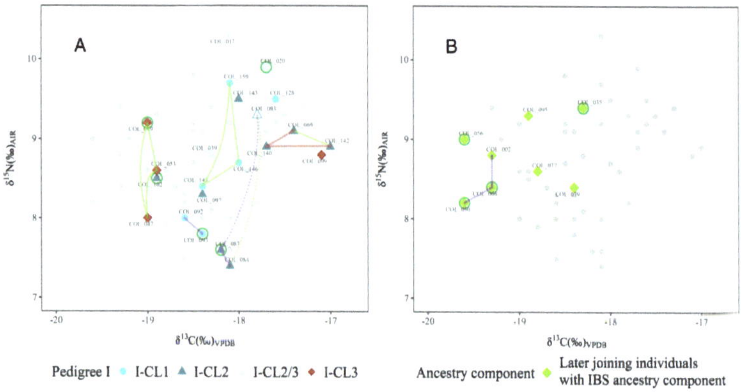

FIGURE 29 *Carbon and nitrogen values from Collegno by pedigree. Tian et al., 'The Role of Emerging Elites in the Formation and Development of Communities after the Fall of the Roman Empire', fig. 5. Copyright © 2024 the Authors. Published by PNAS. This open access article is distributed under a CC BY 4.0 license.*

We have concluded that in all likelihood the members of Pedigree I represent a new elite that founded the community after the Langobard conquest of northern Italy. One might argue that this was a *fara*, but if so, it included both biologically-related individuals and others bound by social ties. The third group, with its elite status but southern ancestry, might represent the rapid acculturation into the new Langobard elite of some elements of the pre-existing Italian elite, but they may also possibly have been part of the heterogenous Pannonian population that had followed Alboin into Italy. We can also see how, across the roughly 150 years that the cemetery was in use, both local individuals and newly arrived groups added to the complexity of the community. However, only multiple studies of similar sites in northern Italy will determine to what extent, if any, Collegno is representative of the new order in the Lombard Kingdom of Italy.

The analysis of sites in Pannonia and Italy may confirm a significant migratory event, but it would be wrong to assume that all of the Pannonian population under Alboin departed for Italy. A significant archaeological study by team member István Koncz has also shown evidence of continuity of what are considered

'Langobard' cultural traditions well beyond 568 in Pannonia – clearly the migration was not a complete demographic break.[57]

The Justinianic plague

The period that corresponds with the Langobard dominance in Pannonia also coincides with the first outbreaks of the Justinianic plague, the first great *Yersinia pestis* pandemic to impact western Eurasia. Studies of the Justinianic plague, its geographic origins, its progress, its mutations and especially the impact of this epidemic on the economy, society and political structures in Eurasia have been the focus of an enormous amount of scholarship and polemic.[58] Much of the scholarship has shifted from the analysis of written sources by philologically trained historians to interdisciplinary, collaborative teams of scientists, paleo climatologists and those rare historians who have taken the time and effort to learn to deal with genomic evidence. We now have a growing number of plague identifications and reconstructed genomes from this epidemic, and we will hear about still more today.

There have also developed opposing interpretative schools. What might be termed the 'maximalists', like Peter Sarris and Michael McCormick, argue that one should take the literary sources seriously in considering the disease's impact, although even among maximalists, whether the plague killed 50 per cent of the Byzantine Empire's population or just 25 to 30 per cent, and the extent to which it brought about a massive depopulation in the Mediterranean and in western Europe is disputed.[59] Some scholars, such as Kyle Harper, have even argued that the plague was so devastating to the Eastern Roman Empire that it was unable to defend itself against Slavs, Persians and Arabs and was thus a major factor in the end of the Empire.[60] The 'minimalists', particularly Lee Mordechai and Merle Eisenberg, argue that while the plague may have had devastating short-term effects in some localities, the effects of the plague were neither uniform nor so catastrophic as to cause substantial mortality at the societal level, not to mention the collapse of states or empires.[61] They argue that the written sources have not been properly contextualized in the rhetorical and ideological frames in which they were written and that evidence from legislation, numismatics, funerary archaeology and epigraphy do not suggest widespread breakdowns in economic, social or cultural practices.

Efforts to resolve these disagreements turn increasingly to analyses of the methods and assumptions of the participants in the debate, but also to such proxy-sources as evidence of climate change that may have influenced the virulence of plague in different areas. Likewise, studies of pollen grains and spores are being investigated to see if, as in the fourteenth century, the plague caused major changes in agriculture due to population decline and abandonment of arable land. Thus far, the results are inconclusive, but do not seem to support uniform, major disruptions.[62]

At the same time, analyses of genetic changes in the observed *Yersinia pestis* bacteria in sixth-century graves are being used to better understand the route by which the plague reached the Mediterranean world. Procopius claimed that it first arrived from East Africa into Egypt, an assumption widely accepted by historians. However, phylogeny of plague genomes suggests that it may have originated in central Asia, possibly in modern Kyrgyzstan.[63] Routes of transmission from central Asia to the west may suggest alternative chronologies and transmission patterns to those observed by literate observers in Constantinople and elsewhere.

Indeed, we are finding abundant evidence of victims of the plague in sixth-century cemeteries from Czechia, Slovakia and Hungary. At Hegykő, in western Hungary, twenty-five of the sixty-five sampled individuals showed clear evidence of the disease.

At other sites, the percentage of identifiable individuals who died of plague varied between 10 and 19 per cent. Given the difficulty of identifying the bacterium in skeletal remains, the number was certainly much higher. The plague seems to have reached the region very early: the first strain identified in Slovakia and western Hungary is the earliest form of the plague and dates from the 540s. The disease returned to the region at least a decade later in a slightly mutated form, claiming still more victims. However, in contrast to the kind of burials that one sees in, say, the Black Death of the fourteenth century, sites such as Hegykő show no evidence of disruption of the social norms. These are no mass burials, but rather these respect in all forms the traditions of burials prior to and after this period. Even in the face of this terrible plague, these communities evidenced an astonishing cultural resiliency.[64]

FIGURE 30 *Map of Hegykő cemetery showing in yellow those who died of* Yersinia pestis. *Reproduced with permission of István Koncz.*

What the effects of the plague were on the populations of central Europe is less easy to assess. The mortality apparently did not prevent the Langobard army from consolidating its control over the Pannonia or prevent it from conquering much of Italy a few generations later. We need many more studies, both of skeletal evidence of plague victims and proxies for possible decline or changes in agricultural productivity to determine to what extent the Justinianic plague contributed to the social and political changes of the sixth century.

The Avars: new masters of Pannonia

Around 558, some 20,000 warriors from a people never before encountered by the Romans arrived north of the Caucasus. Their Khagan Baian sent a delegation to Constantinople, boasting that they were the unconquered Avars and offering to defeat the Romans' enemies in return for gifts and fertile land. They were warmly received by the aged Emperor Justinian. The Balkan provinces were under constant threat from barbarian neighbours across the Danube, and the emperor, in good Roman tradition, granted their demands in return for service against the various hostile polities along the northern frontier. Just who these people were was at the time a question of dispute, and has remained so until today.[65]

The origin of this new population has long remained controversial. Between 402 and 555, a tribal complex, the Rouran Khaganate, controlled a vast, multi-ethnic region including modern Mongolia and Inner Mongolia, as well as parts of north east China, Siberia, Xinjiang and Kazakhstan. Their regional dominance gave them control of the Silk Road across central Asia, and they increased their power through regular raiding of their Chinese neighbours to the south and their subjugation of other tribal groups throughout the region. As a result of their raiding, the Avars were in almost constant conflict with the northern Wei Dynasty, itself founded by the Xianbei, another Steppe people who had become progressively Sinicized. After the split of the northern Wei, the Avars were courted by both the eastern and western Wei for military support, increasing their international importance. However, internal challenges by their subject peoples led to rebellion and their defeat by a Turkic subject population, the Göktürks, and in the 550s their empire was absorbed by this first Turkic Khaganate. According to the emissaries to Justinian, this newly arrived people were the remnants of this great Rouran Empire.

The rulers of the new Turkish Khaganate denied this emphatically. They insisted instead that this people that appeared north of the Black Sea shorty afterwards were not actually the Avars but 'pseudo-Avars' – a mixed group of peoples subordinate to the Turks whom the latter termed Varchorites. The Turks maintained that these peoples had lived in western central Asia but had rebelled against their Turkic masters and appropriated the Avar name to provide them with legitimacy.

Our team undertook an extensive study of some sixty-six individuals from the Pannonia and the Carpathian Basin from both before and after the arrival of the Avars in order to judge the extent of the purported migration and, to the extent possible, the likely origins of this Steppe people.[66] The sample included eight of the richest early Avar period burials as well as other elite sites from the Danube–Tisa interfluve. This region in what is today central Hungary, which seems to have been something of a no-man's land between the Langobard and Gepid kingdoms, appears to have been mostly uninhabited in the sixth century, but became the centre of the Avar Empire. The differences in ancestry between the pre- and Avar-period populations in the region is striking. While the pre-Avar population was largely European, we found that although there was great genetic variability within the Avar-period population, all of the elite individuals have north-east Asian ancestry profiles falling generally within the present-day populations between the Altai to Mongolia. Moreover, when compared with ancient individuals, they show strong affinity with north-east Asian populations, including the one sequenced individual from the Rouran Empire. This suggests that this population may have moved fairly rapidly from the eastern Steppe across the Asian Steppes and

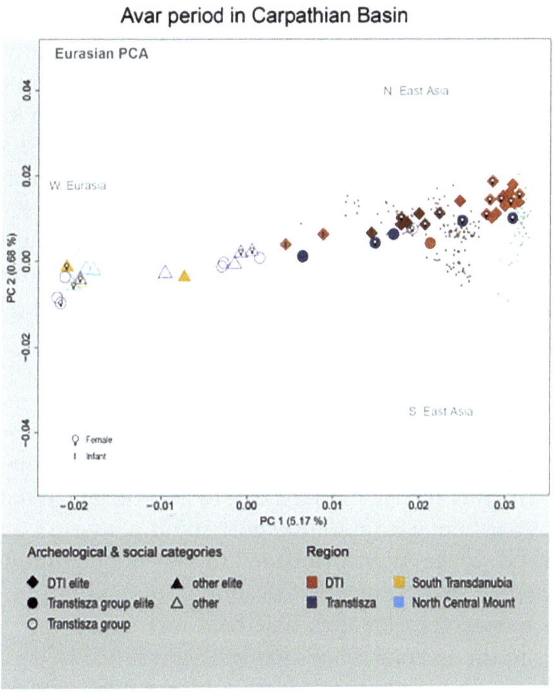

FIGURE 31 *PCA of Avar-period individuals projected onto modern Eurasians. Gnecchi-Ruscone et al., 'Ancient Genomes Reveal Trans-Eurasian Connections between the European Huns and the Xiongnu Empire', fig. 4B. With permission from Elsevier.*

into the west, intermixing to some extent along the way, but the movement seems to have been sufficiently rapid to have maintained very strong evidence of their east Asian origins and, as we shall see, social structures.

The newly arrived Avars proved extremely capable as Roman federates, but Justinian's successor Justin II balked when they returned to Constantinople to demand the right to settle across the Danube. Initially, Baian did not react, focusing instead on subjecting all of their barbarian neighbours and even carrying out attacks on the Franks to the west. He then formed an alliance with the Langobard King Alboin against the Gepids who had been allies of the Romans. Justin II left the Gepids to their fate, and in 567 the Langobards and Avars together destroyed the Gepid kingdom. Alboin absorbed their army into his, while the Romans took advantage of the collapse to reclaim Sirmium, the old Roman capital of Pannonia and the seat of Gepid rule. The following year, as we have noted above, Alboin, for reasons still in dispute, turned over all of his kingdom to the Avars and departed with his people for Italy. Baian proceeded to occupy the former Gepid kingdom and, although he could not force the Romans out of Sirmium, solidified his control of both the former Gepid and Langobard kingdoms while maintaining a cautious peace with Constantinople. Both polities had as common enemies an expansive Turkish Empire and, increasingly, Slavic raiders on the lower Danube who began in 578 to attack and pillage the Balkans.

Peaceful relations did not long last, particularly after the Avars were able to force the Slavic groups into something resembling subordination to them. In the 580s, the Avars renewed their assault on Sirmium, crossing the Danube and Sava rivers, and in 582 the Emperor Tiberius surrendered the city to the Khagan and agreed to pay a heavy tribute worth 80,000 gold solidi per year. Capitalizing on their success, the Avars proceeded to take Singidunum/Belgrade and threatened to advance to Constantinople itself. The emperor was able to negotiate treaties that held this assault off for some years, but in the interval, Slavic raiders – presumably on the order of, or at least with the tacit permission of, the Avars – continued to devastate the Balkans.

The apogee of Avar power came in 626 when a vast Avar cavalry, Slavs in small boats as well as infantry, with Sassanid reinforcements at the ready, besieged Constantinople for over a month. Ultimately unable to defeat the Byzantine fleet or to breach the massive walls with their siege engines, the Avars and their allies were forced to retreat. Thereafter, the Avar Empire drew in upon itself, its period of conquest and expansion at an end.

With the danger of Avar expansion abated, Roman and Byzantine authors lost interest in them and, for the following century and a half, written sources provide little information about the internal affairs of the Khaganate. Only occasional references, primarily in western, Latin texts, mention the Avar Empire until, in the later eighth century, an expanding Frankish Empire under Charlemagne destroyed and absorbed the Avar realm. Here only archaeological and genomic evidence can help elucidate the gradual process by which this conquering elite from the Far East managed to organize, control and gradually merge a largely harmonious cultural tradition among the disparate groups of Roman, Gepid, Bulgar, Slavic and other groups who made up the population of the region.

Our research has provided unprecedented insight into the complex processes by which the Avars came to terms with the inhabitants of their new territory. While burial sites in the fifth and sixth centuries tend to be quite small and may represent transient settlements, by the seventh century, one again encounters large cemeteries that span multiple centuries. In a recent *Nature* article, we studied 424 individuals from four cemeteries in the Great Hungarian Plain and were able to describe a number of large pedigrees spanning nine generations and comprising around 300 individuals.[67] A study of two contemporaneous sites in eastern Austria provided six-generation pedigrees linking 450 individuals.[68] While a pedigree is not the same as a kindred, we were able to show cultural and social relationships among the individuals who are biologically connected in these pedigrees. Within these communities we find that the organization is almost exclusively patrilocal (see Figure 32), while women come from outside of the communities. In Rákóczifalva, one of the central Hungarian sites, we find only two Y chromosome lineages but fifty mtDNA haplogroups, indicating the striking difference between the backgrounds of the men, who share a very similar ancestry, and the women, who were recruited from a wide spectrum of biological kindreds. Nevertheless, there is a clear indication of a deep knowledge of the social ancestry of both men and women. Within these communities we find that there are no cases of marriage within six degrees of kinship. These people

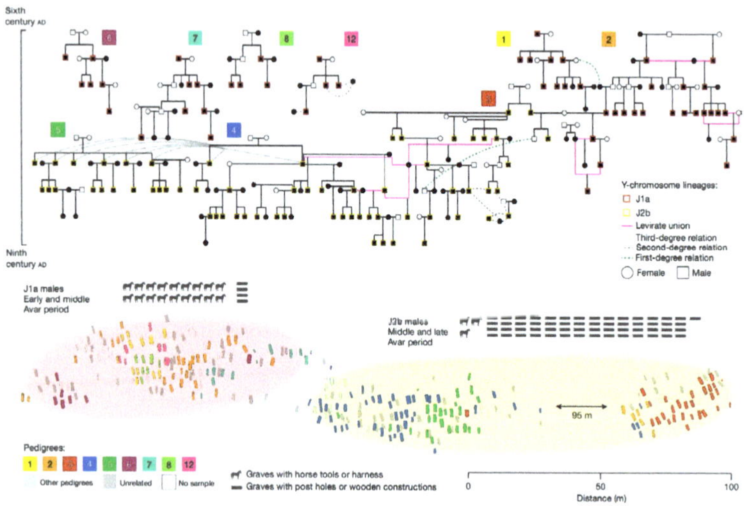

FIGURE 32 *Interconnected individuals in a set of sub-pedigrees. Gnecchi-Ruscone et al., 'Network of Large Pedigrees Reveals Social Practices of Avar Communities', fig. 2. Available under a CC BY 4.0 license.*

had deep knowledge of their entire ancestry as well as that of women brought from the outside.

Through careful examination of the relationships within these extended communities we're also able to recognize certain cultural practices, particularly within the Avar Empire, practices that seem to have been continuations of those from the Asian Steppe. For example, we see the presence of numerous Levirate marriages (shown with pink lines in Figure 32) – that is, marriages in which, should a husband die, the wife will then marry his brother or a stepson or other close male relative of her husband. This is a tradition which existed in central Asia into the early twentieth century and suggests a continuity in western Europe of a kind of social organization transmitted from the Steppe and implanted within the western world.

While these societies may be patrilocal, we can also recognize the essential role of women in binding together different communities. Analysis of IBD networks show that women moving from one community to another play an key role in consolidating larger units within this society.

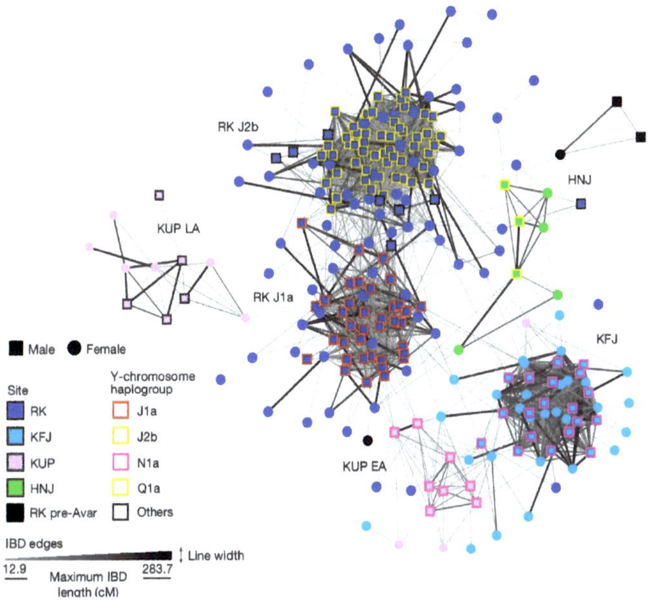

FIGURE 33 *IBD networks showing the role of women in connecting Avar-era communities. Gnecchi-Ruscone et al., 'Network of Large Pedigrees Reveals Social Practices of Avar Communities', fig. 3. Available under a CC BY 4.0 license.*

Ancestry and culture

While there is a correlation between material culture and genetic ancestry visible in sites such as Rákóczifalva, at the western Austria sites of Leobersdorf and Mödling, there is no relationship between material culture and ancestry although the two cemeteries are less than 20 kilometres apart.[69] One finds in both, typical Avar period belt sets, weapons and female ornaments, although in different proportions and slight variations. However, while the population of Mödling was distinctly typically European, the Leobersdorf population, from the sixth to the end of the eighth centuries, retained a markedly Asian genetic profile. Moreover, across these centuries, the women introduced into this patrilocal community, perhaps from central Hungary, shared this background.

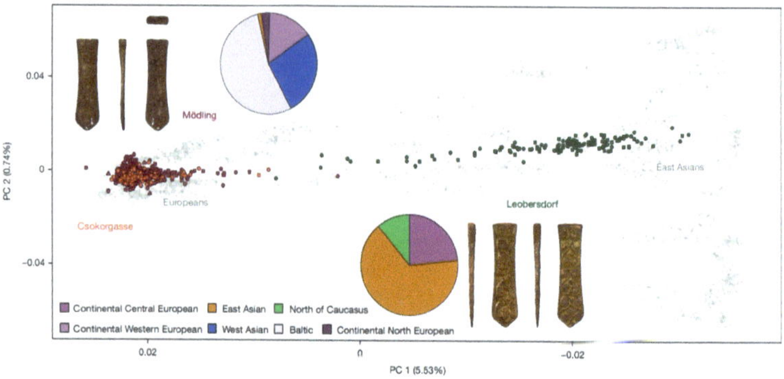

FIGURE 34 *PCA of Mödling, Czokorgasse and Leobersdorf, Austria, showing the genetic distance between two communities sharing a common culture. Ka Wang et al., 'Ancient DNA Reveals Reproductive Barrier Despite Shared Avar-Period Culture', fig. 1. Available under a CC BY 4.0 license.*

However, this practice of selecting partners with a similar genetic background is by no means universal among kindreds with an eastern genetic profile in the Avar Empire. Elsewhere, we are finding unions between people of different origins so frequent that one might suspect that they were deliberately orchestrated.

Thus, across the Avar Empire, we see both the process of maintaining strong links to population centres with significant Asian ancestry, and areas in which this seems to have been consciously avoided. We also recognize that in spite of ancestry, in the course of the later seventh and eighth centuries, the inhabitants of the region adopted a similar culture. They had, in some sense at least, all become Avars, although they may have simultaneously held other forms of identity. And this apparently included, in part at least, that most enigmatic portion of the population who, from the sixth century, appear in Greek and in Latin sources as Slavs.

The creation of the Slavic world

The most enigmatic transformation in the Early Middle Ages was that of Slavization. In recent years there has been considerable debate about the origins and process by which much of central and eastern Europe became Slavicized. It has long been difficult to trace this process and some historians have suggested that, rather than seeing this as a migratory process, we should understand the appearance of the Slavs along the Danube as a transformation of those populations already living in the area who, under pressure from the Byzantine Empire, begin to develop a new, decentralized form of political and social culture.[70] Others have long argued for placing an Urheimat or original homeland in various locations from Ukraine to Poland. Now we are beginning to see very clear evidence of the spread of a new population across the region that extends from modern Slovenia to western Hungary, eastern Austria, Slovakia, Czechia and Germany. This new population shows a relationship between populations in north-eastern Europe in what is today northern Poland.

However, it would be premature to assume that these emigrants shared a uniform Slavic political and cultural tradition. Today, the term 'Slavs' can have either the meaning of those who speak a Slavic language or citizens of Slavic nation-states. However, the term also has a long and complex ideological history both in Pan-Slavic movements and Russian imperialism as well as in western prejudices, who regarded their neighbours to the east and south-east as a culturally inferior collective. Written sources beginning in the sixth and seventh centuries begin to refer to groups termed 'Slavs' or 'Wends'; archaeological complexes show traces of shared practices within what is themed Prague or Korchak culture; and language affinities demonstrate a common Slavic idiom before its divergence into distinct Slavic languages. However, these three need not always coincide and certainly there is no evidence that the people that we refer to collectively as the Slavs would have identified themselves as such.[71]

However this population might have understood itself, the significance of its influence on the demography and culture of all of eastern and south-eastern Europe was enormous. In the Elbe-Saale region that we saw previously to have a population composed of individuals with a western European background, a significant change takes place around 600. In a short time, a new and significant population shift takes place toward north-eastern Europe, as shown in Figure 35.

We find similar shifts across central and eastern Europe, with the percentages of this new population reaching *c.* 46 per cent in the

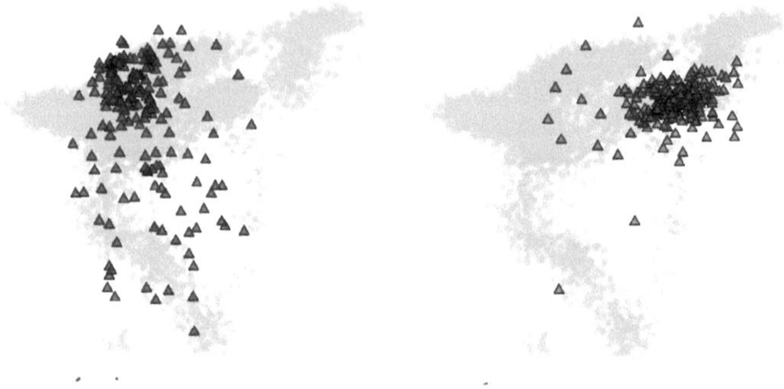

FIGURE 35 *PCA showing shift toward the north-east after 600 in the Elbe-Saale region. After Gretzinger et al., 'Ancient DNA Connects Large-Scale Migration with the Spread of Slavs'. Reproduced with permission of Joscha Gretzinger.*

north-western Balkans, 65 per cent in what is today eastern Germany, and 63 per cent in Poland and northern Ukraine. Although already present prior to the seventh-century to some extent in the region, this component, which is highly similar in all instances, rose to *c.* 27 per cent in the western part of the Avar settlement area at Mödling in modern Austria. In Slovenia we have a dearth of evidence from the crucial seventh and eighth centuries, however by the ninth and tenth centuries again we see a significant new population with a genetic shift toward the north-east, just as we do in the Little Hungarian Plain.

Taken together, all of this is evidence that indeed a significant population shift or shifts took place between the sixth and the ninth centuries that brought populations previously unknown in these parts of Europe from the north-east. All of these populations that share a north-eastern ancestry are remarkably similar, suggesting that an expansion took place within a fairly short time that extended across central and southern Europe. Moreover, these new populations show a different structure from those that preceded them. While biological kinship groups in the older communities were fairly small, in these communities one finds a very tight network of interrelated individuals. In some areas, the previous population appears to have been replaced, although in others one sees a mixture of the new more north-eastern ancestry with the previously existing population.

One might be tempted to term this major demographic event as simply the Slavic migration. However, such a term is problematic for a number of reasons. First, it is hardly a migration in the sense of a discrete group moving from one place to another; it is more of a diffusion or expansion that ultimately included most of central and south-eastern Europe. Nor, as we have said, is it by any means certain that these new arrivals, who seem to have adopted very different cultural traditions, would have seen themselves as part of some greater Slavic community. And of course, neither archaeology nor genetics can explain why this population shift took place. Were they recruited as mercenaries by the Avars, were they fleeing stronger rivals, or were they simply taking advantage of new opportunities offered by population decline and political unrest in central Europe?

Whatever the combination of push and pull factors that brought these people into the Carpathian Basin and adjoining areas, the ways that they adapted to the new and very different political and cultural environments in which they found themselves were by no means uniform. In modern Czechia, within the region that is commonly referred to as Prague-type culture, these new arrivals seem to have been in close cultural contact with Germanic neighbours. While their material culture seems distinct from that of earlier inhabitants, the recent discovery of a set of Germanic runes carved onto a bone suggests that to some extent this population, although originally from north-eastern Europe, was in the process of assimilating some aspects of western Germanic culture.[72] In the area of western Austria, we find communities with a distinct north-eastern genetic characteristic whose material culture is indistinguishable from other Avar khaganate settlements. Clearly, in different regions these new arrivals found different ways of integrating themselves into existing cultural frameworks while maintaining other distinguishing cultural traditions.

Conclusion

Both the methodologies that this brief introduction has presented and the results thus far obtained are but preliminary steps in a new and promising approach to achieving a deeper understanding of the past. Along with the hope for greater success in obtaining meaningful genomic data from greatly degraded specimens, from soil, and even, eventually, from cremated remains, specialists in paleogenomics are actively developing new techniques for analysis. Principle Component Analysis, admixture analyses and identity by descent networks remain rather primitive. They make use of only a small portion of the data that it is now possible to generate, and they are not yet able to make the extremely fine distinctions within populations that we need to recognize minute but significant differences in very closely related populations. Other approaches that focus on microsatellites and rare variants are promising steps forward, but these methods are not yet robust enough to overcome the challenges of working with such degraded and damaged genetic material.

The choices of samples for analysis are also only at the beginning. While some laboratories pride themselves on collecting and analysing thousands of samples across great stretches of time and space, these extensive studies cannot recreate the detailed pedigrees, the short- and long-distance marriage patterns, or the cultural norms that shape the genetic profiles we wish to understand. Our experience suggests that intensive focus on whole cemetery analyses combining all types of evidence is the best way to analyse the social and cultural systems of our subjects. However, intensive analysis is extremely time-consuming. The archaeological analysis, the construction of pedigrees and the comparison of archaeological, isotopic and genomic patterns cannot yet be automated. Thus, even in our study of some 150 cemeteries and 7,500 individuals, we are only looking at a small portion of the over 100,000 skeletal remains available in museums and depositories. Moreover, these studies have focused exclusively on DNA evidence from burials. We have not begun to look for DNA in dwellings and villages where our subjects lived. One can hope that in the future, collaboration with specialists in settlement archaeology might eventually to be able to link households where individuals lived with those whose graves we have studied. To date, however, we do not yet have the tools or the techniques to accomplish this.

We continue to struggle with the challenge of working across disciplinary boundaries, not only because the methodologies that we employ are so different, but also because the professional expectations and demands of different disciplines are often incompatible. Geneticists focus on dense, high-profile publications whose average length is around twelve pages, while archaeologists and historians expect to produce more detailed and complex monographs that may run to hundreds of pages. Natural scientists are accustomed to publications of collective authorship, the number of authors often in the dozens, while primary credit goes to the first author. But who should be the first author in a publication that is truly interdisciplinary? Should it be the geneticist who did the statistical analyses, the archaeologist who identified, classified and analysed each tomb, or the isotopic specialist who has demonstrated the different patterns of mobility and diet within the community? These are non-trivial questions, because for young scholars and scientists, their careers depend on how they are credited for what may have been years of work within a team.

While the participants themselves may have overcome the dangerous, essentializing tendencies of earlier attempts to write history from genetics, the danger that their results will be misconstrued either intentionally or by ignorance, by both scholars and the wider public, remains. The very language that must be used to describe and to interpret results is in constant danger of seeming to revert to discredited and even dangerous ways of interpretation. Migration vs. diffusion; kinship vs. biological relatedness; ethnicity vs. genetic population; identity vs. heterogeneity – all of these and more continue to pose the possibility of misinterpretation or overinterpretation, with the danger that simplistic conclusions may discredit even the most sophisticated analysis. The temptation to classify individuals by ethnic labels and to explain cultural and genomic change by mass migration without adequately considering alternatives continue to challenge everyone involved in such projects.

Anxieties among historians and archaeologists who fear the challenges to their established theories or who fear that natural science is reducing the complexity of human history to mere statistical models or biology are very real. However, I hope that I have shown in the chapters above that complexity, hybridity and movement, be it across great distances or from one village to the next, characterize European societies well before the disappearance of the Roman Empire and well into the Middle Ages. At the same time, the very fact that these communities managed to continue their cultural practices even in the face of movement, transformation and even catastrophe leads to reflections on the fact that our natural scientific approaches, far from reducing these societies to simple biology, rather highlight the importance of culture, of human choice and resilience across these tumultuous centuries. Not only could they face massive deaths without abandoning the proper treatment of the departed, but they could retain a deep knowledge of their families, and those of others, across time and space. They could adopt traditions of new, dominant elites – artificial cranial deformation or Avar-style belt sets for example – without giving up their own particular traditions, foodways and values. We see migrants from north-eastern Europe adopting new cultural practices but selectively incorporating them as they adjust to new lands and new opportunities, even while maintaining much of their heritage. Human decisions, not biological determinism, forged the world that we study. To paraphrase Shakespeare's Cassius, for the peoples of the early medieval Carpathian Basin as for us today, their fates were not in their genes but in themselves.

NOTES

Introduction

1 Elizabeth D. Jones, *Ancient DNA: The Making of a Celebrity Science* (New Haven, CT, and London: Yale University Press, 2022).

2 Johannes Krause and Thomas Trappe, *Hybris: Die Reise der Menschheit: zwischen Aufbruch und Scheitern*. 4. Aufl. (Berlin: Propyläen. 2021); English edition: *Hubris: The Rise, Fall, and Future of Humanity* (Cambridge: Polity Press, 2024).

3 Dario Internullo, 'Du papyrus au parchemin: Les origines médiévales de la mémoire archivistique en Europe occidentale', *Annales HSS* 74, nos 3–4 (2019): 523–57.

4 See Wilfried Nippel, *Griechen, Barbaren und 'Wilde': Alte Geschichte und Sozialanthropologie* (Frankfurt am Main: Fischer, 1990); Walter Pohl, 'Telling the Difference: Signs of Ethnic Identity', in Walter Pohl and Helmut Reimitz, eds, *Strategies of Distinction: The Construction of Ethnic Communities, 300–800*, 17–69 (Leiden: Brill, 1998); Patrick J. Geary, *The Myth of Nations: The Medieval Origins of Europe* (Princeton, NJ: Princeton University Press, 2002), 57–84; Michael Maas, *The Conqueror's Gift: Roman Ethnography and the End of Antiquity* (Princeton, NJ: Princeton University Press, 2025).

1 The Dangerous Legacy of Racialized History

1 Tony Waldron, 'DNA in Bones', *International Journal of Osteoarchaeology* 1, no. 2 (1991): 155–6. See also Elsbeth Bösl, *Doing Ancient DNA: Zur Wissenschaftsgeschichte der aDNA-Forschung*, 1st edn. Histoire 111 (Bielefeld: Transcript Verlag, 2017), 237.

2 Two of his classic works were Gustaf Kossinna, *Ursprung und Verbreitung der Germanen in vor-und frühgeschichtlicher Zeit*,

Mannus-Bibliothek no. 6 (Leipzig: Mannus-Bibliothek, 1928), and *Die deutsche Vorgeschichte: eine hervorragend nationale Wissenschaft* (Würzburg: C. Kabitzsch, 1912).

3 A noted archaeologist of his day prior to entering politics, his methodology is demonstrated in his *Epoka kamienia na wydmach wschodniej części Wyżyny Małopolskiej* [The Stone Age on the dunes of the eastern part of the Lesser Poland Upland] (Lwów: Książnica polska, 1923). See Sebastian Brather, *Archäologie der westlichen Slawen: Siedlung, Wirtschaft und Gesellschaft im früh- und hochmittelalterlichen Ostmitteleuropa* (Berlin and New York: De Gruyter, 2008).

4 On Childe, see David R. Harris, ed., *The Archaeology of V. Gordon Childe: Contemporary Perspectives* (London: University College London, 1994).

5 Alexander Gramsch, 'Culture, change, identity. Approaches to the interpretation of cultural change', *Anthropologie* 53 (2015): 341–9.

6 For a brief overview of the vast literature on nineteenth-century national romanticism, see Geary, *Myth of Nations*.

7 Caroli Linnaei, *Systema naturae, sive regna tria naturae systematice proposita per classes, ordines, genera, & species* (Leiden: Theodorum Haak, 1735).

8 John Pinkerton, *A Dissertation on the Origin and Progress of the Scythians or Goths, Being an Introduction to the Ancient and Modern History of Europe* (London: John Nichols, for George Nicol, Pall-Mall, 1787), 123. On Pinkerton, see Paul Stock, '"Almost a Separate Race": Racial Thought and the Idea of Europe in British Encyclopedias and Histories, 1771–1830', *Modern Intellectual History* 8 (April 2011): 1, 3–29, esp. 20–5.

9 Arthur de Gobineau, *Essai sur l'inégalité des races humaines*, 4 vols (Paris: Imprimerie de Firmin Didot frères, 1853).

10 For a comprehensive summary of nineteenth-century racial identities in Europe, see Richard McMahon, *The Races of Europe: Construction of National Identities in the Social Sciences, 1839–1939* (London: Palgrave Macmillan, 2016).

11 For a comprehensive overview, see James Poskett, *Materials of the Mind: Phrenology, Race, and the Global History of Science, 1815–1920* (Chicago: University of Chicago Press, 2019).

12 These collections are beginning to be the focus of critical study. See the report of a 2018 exhibition focused on the collection from 8,000 skulls in the collection of the Natural History Museum of Vienna at the Edinburgh College of Art: Tal Adler, Linda Fibiger, John Harris,

Maria Teschler-Nicola, Joan Smith and Anna Szöke, 'Dead Images. Facing the history, ethics and politics of European skull collections', in M. Hamm and K. Schönberger, eds, *Contentious Heritages and Arts: A Critical Companion*, 63–8 (Klagenfurt: Wieser Verlag, 2012). For the American version of this phenomenon, see Ann Fabian, *The Skull Collectors: Race, Science, and America's Unburied Dead* (Chicago: University of Chicago Press, 2010).

13 For the complex implications of this tradition into the present, see Keith Wailoo, Alondra Nelson and Catherine Lee, eds, *Genetics and the Unsettled Past: The Collision of DNA, Race, and History* (New Brunswick, NJ: Rutgers University Press, 2012).

14 For a sympathetic but not uncritical treatment of the tradition of settlement archaeology, see Florin Curta, 'From Kossinna to Bromley: ethnogenesis in Slavic archaeology', in Andrew Gillett, ed., *On Barbarian Identity: Critical Approaches to Ethnicity in the Early Middle Ages*, 201–18 (Turnhout, Belgium: Brepols, 2002).

15 Kossinna, *Ursprung und Verbreitung der Germanen*, 167.

16 'Die Körperlichen Reste der Urbewohner unseres Landes, die wir hier so genau kennen gelernt haben, wie der heutige Stand unserer Wissenschaft es zulässt, lehren, von welchen Ahnen wir abstammen und von welchen nicht. Aber noch Größeres leistet ja die Rassenkunde insofern, als sie nicht nur die körperlichen, sondern auch die seelischen und geistigen Eigenheiten der heutigen Rassen, also die bedeutungsvollen Unterschiede der Rassen nach dieser Richtung hin erkennen lässt.' Kossinna, *Ursprung und Verbreitung der Germanen*, 125.

17 The recent literature on early medieval ethnicity and migration is enormous and rapidly expanding. Early contributions were made by Herwig Wolfram, both in his own scholarship as in 'Zur Ansiedlung reichsangehöriger Föderaten', *Mitteilungen des Instituts für Österreichische Geschichtsforschung* 91 (1983): 5–35; 'Ethnogenesen im frühmittelalterlichen Donau- und Ostalpenraum (6. bis 10. Jahrhundert)', in Helmut Beumann and Werner Schröder, eds, *Frühmittelalterliche Ethnogenese im Alpenraum*, Nationes 5, 97–151 (Sigmaringen: J. Thorbecke, 1985); and in his classic *Die Goten und ihre Geschichte* 4. Durchgesehene und aktualisierte Auflage, Originalausgabe. Beck Wissen (Munich: C.H. Beck, 2022), as well as in various collaborations he launched, such as Herwig Wolfram and Andreas Schwarcz, eds, *Anerkennung und Integration. Zu den wirtschaftlichen Grundlagen der Völkerwanderungszeit, 400–600*, Denkschriften der Österreichischen Akademie der Wissenschaften, phil. hist. Kl. 193 (Vienna, 1988). More recent significant contributions include those of Walter Pohl, many of which appeared in the context of the European Science Foundation's project 'The Transformation of the Roman World', including Walter Pohl and Helmut Reimitz, eds, *Strategies of Distinction: The Construction of Ethnic Communities, 300–800*, The Transformation of the Roman World 2 (Leiden, Boston and Cologne, 1998) and Walter Pohl, ed., *Kingdoms of the Empire: The Integration of Barbarians in Late Antiquity*, The Transformation of the Roman World 1 (Leiden, New York and Cologne, 1997), as well as his own studies including *Die Awaren. Ein Steppenvolk in Mitteleuropa, 567–822 n. Chr.* (Munich: Beck, Anglo 1988), revised and expanded as *The Avars: A Steppe Empire in Central Europe, 567–822* (Ithaca, NY: Cornell University Press, 2018); 'Conceptions of ethnicity in early medieval studies', *Archaeologia Polona* 29 (1991): 39–49, and 'Ethnicity, theory and tradition: a response', in Andrew Gillett, ed., *On Barbarian Identity: Critical Approaches to Ethnicity in the Early Middle Ages*, 122–239 (Turnhout, Belgium: Brepols, 2002). More recently, Michael Borgolte has written on the history of migration in trans-cultural perspective, as in 'Migrationen als transkulturelle Verflechtungen im mittelalterlichen Europa. Ein neuer Pflug für alte Forschungsfelder', *Historische Zeitschrift* 289 (2009): 261–85.

18 Michael Borgolte, 'Mythos Völkerwanderung: Migration oder Expansion bei den "Ursprüngen Europas"', *Viator* 41 (Multilingual) (2010): 23–48.

19 Particularly significant in this regard is the work of Sebastian Brather, 'Ethnische Identitäten als Konstrukte der frühgeschichtlichen Archäologie', *Germania* 78 (2000): 139–77, and Guy Halsall (review article), 'Movers and Shakers: The Barbarians and the Fall of Rome', *Early Medieval Europe* 8 (1999): 131–25, and his 'Archaeology and the late Roman frontier in Northern Gaul: The so-called "Föderatengräber" revisited', in Walter Pohl and Helmut Reimitz, eds, *Grenze und Differenz im frühen Mittelalter*, Forschungen zur Geschichte des Mittelalters 1, 167–80 (Vienna, 2000).

20 Herwig Wolfram, *The Roman Empire and Its Germanic Peoples* (Berkeley and Los Angeles: University of California Press, 1990). Translation of *Das Römerreich und seine Germanen: eine Erzählung von Herkunft und Ankunft* (Vienna: Böhlau Verlag, 2018).

21 Guy Halsall, *Barbarian Migrations and the Roman West 376–568*. Cambridge Medieval Textbooks (Cambridge: Cambridge University Press, 2007), 34.

22 Ehud Lamm, Oren Harman and Sophie Juliane Veigl, 'Before Watson and Crick in 1953 Came Friedrich Miescher in 1869', *Genetics* 215, no. 2 (1 June 2020): 291–6.

23 Among his early work on genetics and human population is Albert J. Ammerman and L. L. Cavalli-Sforza, *The Neolithic Transition and the Genetics of Populations in Europe* (Princeton, NJ: Princeton University Press, 1984). For a general audience, he wrote *Genes, Peoples, and Languages* (New York: North Point Press, 2000) to present his approach more widely.

24 Susanne E. Hakenbeck, 'Genetics, archaeology and the far right: an unholy Trinity', *World Archaeology* 51, no. 4 (August 2019): 517–27. See also Volker Heyd, 'Kossinna's smile', *Antiquity* 91, no. 356 (2017): 348–59.

25 Morten E. Allentoft et al., 'Population genomics of Bronze Age Eurasia', *Nature* 522, no. 7555 (June 2015): 167–72.

26 Wolfgang Haak Iosif Lazaridis, Nick Patterson, Nadin Rohland, Swapan Mallick, Bastien Llamas, Guido Brandt et al., 'Massive Migration from the Steppe Was a Source for Indo-European Languages in Europe', *Nature* 522, no. 7555 (June 2015): 207–11.

27 Matthew P. Williams and Christian D. Huber, 'The genomic footprints of migration: how ancient DNA reveals our history of mobility', *Genome Biology* 26, no. 206 (2025).

28 An outstanding example of a study showing the genetic complexity of populations is Anja Furtwängler et al., 'Ancient genomes reveal social and genetic structure of Late Neolithic Switzerland', *Nature Communications* 11, no. 1 (2020): 1915, which analyses genome-wide data from ninety-six Neolithic and Early Bronze Age individuals from Switzerland, southern Germany and Alsace, as well as one Early Iron Age individual and one Roman-era individual. The study is careful not to simplify or essentialize the individuals in the study by such labels, but compares them to the 'Yamnaya' complex, 'Bell Beaker populations' and 'Corded Ware' groups.

29 See Megan Gannon, 'When Ancient DNA Gets Politicized', *Smithsonian Magazine*, 12 July 2019; Howard Wolinsky, 'Ancient DNA and contemporary politics: The analysis of ancient DNA challenges long-held beliefs about identity and history with potential for political abuse', *EMBO Reports* 20, no. 12 (December 2019).

30 See especially Jörg Feuchter, 'Für einen kritischen Dialog zwischen Geschichtswissenschaft und genetic history', *NTM Zeitschrift für Geschichte der Wissenschaften, Technik und Medizin* 26 (2018): Heft 3, 339–44; Elsbeth Bösl and Jörg Feuchter, 'Genetic History – Eine Herausforderung für die Geschichtswissenschaften', *Neue Politische Literatur* 64, no. 2 (July 2019): 237–68; and Jörg Feuchter, 'The Middle Ages in the Genetics Lab', in Chris Jones, Conor Kostick and

Klaus Oschema, eds, *Making the Medieval Relevant*, 99–112 (Berlin and Boston: De Gruyter, 2019).

2 Genetic Data as Historical Data

1 Charles-Victor Langlois and Charles Seignobos, *Introduction aux études historiques* (Paris: Hachette, 1898), 13. On the history of this phrase, see above all Lucien Febvre, *Combats pour l'histoire* (Paris: A. Colin, 1965), 4–5, where he rightly remarks that such a phrase, 'par un lien étroit, elle liait l'histoire à l'écriture – et c'était le moment où la préhistoire, au nom bizarrement significatif, s'employait à rédiger, *sans textes*, le plus long des chapitres de l'histoire humaine'. Henning Trüper has attempted to deconstruct Febvre's objections in his *Topography of a Method: François Louis Ganshof and the Writing of History* 1. Auflage. Historische Wissensforschung 2 (Tübingen: Mohr Siebeck, 2014), 17–19, but he seems to have missed Febvre's essential point that documents, texts, are but one source for the writing of history. In his *The History Written on the Classical Greek Body* (Cambridge: Cambridge University Press, 2011), Robin Osborne likewise seems to have missed Febvre's point, continuing to make the artificial distinction between historians and archaeologists: 'What distinguished historians from archaeologists is that they study the past on the basis of the evidence of texts, rather than of material remains' (6). Osborne continues that 'the different approach of archaeologists and of historians is masked by the fact that most of the time they study different periods of the past. Archaeologists concentrate their efforts upon those periods of the past for which there is little or no external evidence upon what is sometimes called "prehistory." Historians operate only with those past societies which have left written records.' Neither premise is correct: historians, as we shall see, have long worked with material as well as written sources, and historians are involved in recovering the history of societies without texts just as archaeologists are involved in expanding our understanding of textual societies in ways that only material culture can allow.

2 The classic study of oral history remains that of the Africanist Jan Vansina, *Oral Tradition as History* (Madison: University of Wisconsin Press, 1985).

3 For an important recent summary, see David Reich, *Who We Are and How We Got Here: Ancient DNA and the New Science of the Human Past* (New York: Pantheon, 2018).

4 Iosif Lazaridis, Nick Patterson, Alissa Mittnik, Gabriel Renaud, Swapan Mallick, Karola Kirsanow, Peter H. Sudmant et al., 'Ancient Human Genomes Suggest Three Ancestral Populations for Present-Day Europeans', *Nature* 513, no. 7518 (September 2014): 409–13.

5 Eugene A. Foster, M. A. Jobling, P. G. Taylor, P. Donnelly, P. De Knijff, Rene Mieremet, T. Zerjal and C. Tyler-Smith, 'Jefferson Fathered Slave's Last Child', *Nature* 396, no. 6706 (November 1998): 27–8.

6 Turi E. King, Gloria Gonzalez Fortes, Patricia Balaresque, Mark G. Thomas, David Balding, Pierpaolo Maisano Delser, Rita Neumann et al., 'Identification of the Remains of King Richard III', *Nature Communications* 5, no. 1 (December 2014): 5631.

7 A. W. F. Edwards and L. L. Cavalli-Sforza, 'Reconstruction of evolutionary trees', in V. H. Heywood and J. McNeill, eds, *Phenetic and Phylogenetic Classification*, 67–76. Systematics Association pub. no. 6 (London: Systematics Association, 1964).

8 Russell Higuchi, Barbara Bowman, Mary Freiberger, Oliver A. Ryder and Allan C. Wilson, 'DNA sequences from the quagga, an extinct member of the horse family', *Nature* 312 (1984): 282–4.

9 Bruce Winney Abdelhamid Boumertit, Tammy Day, Dan Davison, Chikodi Echeta, Irina Evseeva, Katarzyna Hutnik et al., 'People of the British Isles: Preliminary Analysis of Genotypes and Surnames in a UK-Control Population', *European Journal of Human Genetics* 20, no. 2 (February 2012): 203–10.

10 Csanád Bálint, 'Some Problems in Genetic Research on Hungarian Ethnogenesis', *Acta Archaeologica* 61, no. 1: 283–94.

11 Matthew R. Nelson, Katarzyna Bryc, Karen S. King, Amit Indap, Adam R. Boyko, John Novembre, Linda P. Briley et al., 'The Population Reference Sample, POPRES: A Resource for Population, Disease, and Pharmacological Genetics Research', *American Journal of Human Genetics* 83, no. 3 (September 2008): 347–58.

12 Alan Cooper and Hendrik N. Poinar, 'Ancient DNA: Do It Right or Not at All', *Science Magazine* (18 August 2000): 1130–40.

13 Ron Pinhasi, Daniel Fernandes, Kendra Sirak, Mario Novak, Sarah Connell, Songül Alpaslan-Roodenberg, Fokke Gerritsen et al., 'Optimal Ancient DNA Yields from the Inner Ear Part of the Human Petrous Bone', *PLOS ONE* 10, no. 6 (June 2015).

14 H. B. Hansen P. B. Damgaard, A. Margaryan, Jesper Stenderup, Niels Lynnerup, Eske Willerslev and Morten E. Allentoft, 'Comparing Ancient DNA Preservation in Petrous Bone and Tooth Cementum', *PLoS One* 12, no. 1 (January 2017): e0170940; Jamal Ibrahim, Vlad Brumfeld, Yoseph Addadi, Sarah Rubin, Steve Weiner and Elisabetta

Boaretto, 'The Petrous Bone Contains High Concentrations of Osteocytes: One Possible Reason Why Ancient DNA Is Better Preserved in This Bone', *PLOS ONE* 17, no. 10 (October 2022).

15 This discussion is expanded in Patrick J. Geary, 'La femme de la tombe 087 à Collegno: La paléogénomique au service de l'histoire d'une communauté en Italie lombarde', *Mémoires de la Société nationale des antiquaires de France*, in press.

16 Vitor Sousa and Jody Hey, 'Understanding the origin of species with genome-scale data: modelling gene flow', *Nature Reviews Genetics* 14, no. 6 (June 2013): 404–14.

3 Making Sense of Genomic Data

1 Pille Hallast, Anastasia Agdzhoyan, Oleg Balanovsky, Yali Xue and Chris Tyler-Smith, 'A Southeast Asian Origin for Present-Day Non-African Human Y Chromosomes', *Human Genetics* 140, no. 2 (February 2021): 299–307.

2 Y Chromosome Consortium, 'A Nomenclature System for the Tree of Human Y-Chromosomal Binary Haplogroups', *Genome Research* 12, no. 2 (February 2002): 339–48.

3 B. Navarro-López, E. Granizo-Rodríguez, L. Palencia-Madrid, C. Raffone, M. Baeta and M. M. de Pancorbo, 'Phylogeographic review of Y chromosome haplogroups in Europe', *International Journal of Legal Medicine* 135, no. 5 (September 2021): 1675–84.

4 Guido Alberto Gnecchi-Ruscone, Zsófia Rácz, Levente Samu, Tamás Szeniczey, Norbert Faragó, Corina Knipper, Ronny Friedrich et al., 'Network of Large Pedigrees Reveals Social Practices of Avar Communities', *Nature* 629, no. 8011 (May 2024): 376–83.

5 For a brief introduction, see Jake Lever, Martin Krzywinski and Naomi Altma, 'Principal component analysis', *Nature Methods* 14 (2017): 641–2. On issues concerning PCA and ancient DNA, see David Reich, Alkes L. Price and Nick Patterson, 'Principal component analysis of genetic data', *Nature Genetics* 40 (2008): 491–2.

6 For a technical discussion of the use of PCA in population genetics, see Nick Patterson, Alkes L. Price and David Reich, 'Population Structure and Eigenanalysis', *PLOS Genetics* 2, no. 12 (2006).

7 P. Menozzi, A. Piazza and L. Cavalli-Sforza, 'Synthetic Maps of Human Gene Frequencies in Europeans: These maps indicate that early farmers of the Near East spread to all of Europe in the Neolithic', *Science* 201, no. 4358 (1978): 786–92.

8 John Novembre, Toby Johnson, Katarzyna Bryc, Zoltán Kutalik, Adam R. Boyko, Adam Auton, Amit Indap et al., 'Genes Mirror Geography within Europe', *Nature* 456, no. 7218 (November 2008): 98–101.

9 Matthew R. Nelson, Katarzyna Bryc, Karen S. King, Amit Indap, Adam R. Boyko, John Novembre, Linda P. Briley et al., 'The Population Reference Sample, POPRES: A Resource for Population, Disease, and Pharmacological Genetics Research', *American Journal of Human Genetics* 83, no. 3 (September 2008): 347–58.

10 1000 Genomes Project Consortium, A. Auton, L. D. Brooks, R. M. Durbin, E. P. Garrison, H. M. Kang, J. O. Korbel, J. L. Marchini, S. McCarthy, G. A. McVean and G. R. Abecasis, 'A global reference for human genetic variation', *Nature* 526 (2015): 68–74.

11 Swapan Mallick, Heng Li, Mark Lipson, Iain Mathieson, Melissa Gymrek, Fernando Racimo, Mengyao Zhao et al., 'The Simons Genome Diversity Project: 300 Genomes from 142 Diverse Populations', *Nature* 538, no. 7624 (October 2016): 201–6.

12 Nik Patterson, Priya Moorjani, Yontao Luo, Swapan Mallick, Nadin Rohland, Yiping Zhan, Teri Genschoreck, Teresa Webster and David Reich, 'Ancient Admixture in Human History', *Genetics* 192, no. 3 (November 2012): 1065–93.

13 Eduardo Amorim, Stefania Vai, Cosimo Posth, Alessandra Modi, István Koncz, Susanne Hakenbeck, Maria Cristina La Rocca et al., 'Understanding 6th-Century Barbarian Social Organization and Migration through Paleogenomics', *Nature Communications* 9, no. 1 (September 2018): 3547.

14 Yijie Tian, István Koncz, Sarah Defant, Caterina Giostra, Deven N. Vyas, Arkadiusz Sołtysiak, Luisella Pejrani Baricco et al., 'The role of emerging elites in the formation and development of communities after the fall of the Roman Empire', *Proceedings of the National Academy of Sciences* 121, no. 36 (September 2024).

15 Mark L. Lipson, 'Interpreting F-Statistics and Admixture Graphs: Theory and Examples', Preprint, 15 March 2020.

16 1000 Genomes Project Consortium, Corresponding authors, Adam Auton, Gonçalo R. Abecasis, Steering committee, David M. Altshuler, Richard M. Durbin et al., 'A Global Reference for Human Genetic Variation', *Nature* 526, no. 7571 (October 2015): 68–74.

17 David H. Alexander, John Novembre and Kenneth Lange, 'Fast Model-Based Estimation of Ancestry in Unrelated Individuals', *Genome Research* 19, no. 9 (September 2009): 1655–64; Brian K. Maples, Simon Gravel, Eimear E. Kenny, Carlos D. Bustamante,

'RFMix: A Discriminative Modeling Approach for Rapid and Robust Local-Ancestry Inference', *American Journal of Human Genetics* 93, no. 2 (August 2013): 278–88.

18 Umberto Esposito, Ranajit Das, Syakir Syed, Mehdi Pirooznia and Eran Elhaik, 'Ancient Ancestry Informative Markers for Identifying Fine-Scale Ancient Population Structure in Eurasians', *Genes* 9, no. 12 (December 2018): 625; Nick Patterson, Priya Moorjani, Yontao Luo, Swapan Mallick, Nadin Rohland, Yiping Zhan, Teri Genschoreck, Teresa Webster and David Reich, 'Ancient Admixture in Human History', *Genetics* 192, no. 3 (November 2012): 1065–93.

19 Among other discussions, see Stefanie Eisenmann, Eszter Bánffy, Peter Van Dommelen, Kerstin P. Hofmann, Joseph Maran, Iosif Lazaridis, Alissa Mittnik et al., 'Reconciling Material Cultures in Archaeology with Genetic Data: The Nomenclature of Clusters Emerging from Archaeogenomic Analysis', *Scientific Reports* 8, no. 1 (August 2018): 13003; Clara Lu, Rabeeya Ahmed, Amel Lamri and Sonia S. Anand, 'Use of race, ethnicity, and ancestry data in health research', *PLOS Global Public Health* 2, no. 9 (15 September 2002).

20 This is the approach employed by the software tool READ (Relationship Estimation from Ancient DNA). See Jose Manuel Monroy Kuhn, Mattias Jakobsson and Torsten Günther, 'Estimating genetic kin relationships in prehistoric populations', *PLOS One* 13, no. 4 (April 2018).

21 Michail Lipatov, Komal Sanjeev, Rob Patro and Krishna R Veeramah, 'Maximum Likelihood Estimation of Biological Relatedness from Low Coverage Sequencing Data', Preprint, 29 July 2015.

22 Harald Ringbauer, John Novembre and Matthias Steinrücken, 'Parental relatedness through time revealed by runs of homozygosity in ancient DNA', *Nature Communications* 12, no. 1 (September 2021): 5425; Harald Ringbauer, Yilei Huang, Ali Akbari, Swapan Mallck, Iñigo Olalde, Nick Patterson and David Reich, 'Accurate detection of identity-by-descent segments in human ancient DNA', *Nature Genetics* 56, no. 1 (January 2024): 143–51.

23 Maike L. Morrison, Nicolas Alcala and Noah A. Rosenberg, 'FSTRUCT : An FST-based Tool for Measuring Ancestry Variation in Inference of Population Structure', *Molecular Ecology Resources* 22, no. 7 (October 2022): 2614–26.

24 Sharon R. Browning and Brian L. Browning, 'Accurate Non-Parametric Estimation of Recent Effective Population Size from Segments of Identity by Descent', *American Journal of Human Genetics* 97, no. 3 (September 2015): 404–18.

25 Po-Ru Loh, Mark Lipson, Nick Patterson, Priya Moorjani, Joseph K Pickrell, David Reich and Bonnie Berger, 'Inferring Admixture Histories of Human Populations Using Linkage Disequilibrium', *Genetics* 193, no. 4 (April 2013): 1233–54.

26 Priya Moorjani, Sriram Sankararaman, Qiaomei Fu, Molly Przeworski, Nick Patterson and David Reich, 'A Genetic Method for Dating Ancient Genomes Provides a Direct Estimate of Human Generation Interval in the Last 45,000 Years', *Proceedings of the National Academy of Sciences* 113, no. 20 (May 2016): 5652–7.

27 Leo Speidel, Marina Silva, Thomas Booth, Ben Raffield, Kyriaki Anastasiadou, Christopher Barrington, Anders Götherström, Peter Heather and Pontus Skoglund, 'High-Resolution Genomic History of Early Medieval Europe', *Nature* 637, no. 8044 (January 2025): 118–26.

4 Ancient DNA and the Early Medieval Transition

1 Margaret L. Antonio, Ziyue Gao, Hannah M. Moots, Michaela Lucci, Francesca Candilio, Susanna Sawyer, Victoria Oberreiter et al., 'Ancient Rome: A Genetic Crossroads of Europe and the Mediterranean', *Science* 366, no. 6466 (November 2019): 708–14.

2 Iñigo Olalde, Swapan Mallick, Nick Patterson, Nadin Rohland, Vanessa Villalba-Mouco, Marina Silva, Katharina Dulias, et al., 'The Genomic History of the Iberian Peninsula over the Past 8000 Years', *Science* 363, no. 6432 (March 2019): 1230–4.

3 Margaret L. Antonio, Clemens L. Weiß, Ziyue Gao, Susanna Sawyer, Victoria Oberreiter, Hannah M. Moots, Jeffrey P. Spence et al., 'Stable Population Structure in Europe since the Iron Age, despite High Mobility', *eLife* 13 (January 2024).

4 Among others, see Michael E. Weale, Deborah A. Weiss, Rolf F. Jager, Neil Bradman and Mark G. Thomas, 'Y Chromosome Evidence for Anglo-Saxon Mass Migration', *Molecular Biology and Evolution* 19, no. 7 (July 2002): 1008–21; Mark G. Thomas, P. H. Stumpf and Heinrich Härke, 'Evidence for an Apartheid-like Social Structure in Early Anglo-Saxon England', *Proceedings of the Royal Society B: Biological Sciences* 273, no. 1601 (October 2006): 2651–7. On these and other early studies, see Patrick J. Geary and Krishna Veeramah, 'Mapping European Population Movement through Genomic Research', *Medieval Worlds* 4 (2016): 65–78.

5 Stephan Schiffels, Wolfgang Haak, Pirita Paajanen, Bastien Llamas, Elizabeth Popescu, Louise Loe, Rachel Clarke et al., 'Iron Age and Anglo-Saxon Genomes from East England Reveal British Migration History', *Nature Communications* 7, no. 1 (January 2016): 10408.

6 See the summary by Joscha Gretzinger and Stephan Schiffels, 'A Glimpse into Darkness: Population Genetics of the European Middle Ages', *Neue Studien zur Sachsenforschung 11, New Narratives for the First Millennium AD?: Alte und neue Perspektiven der archäologischen Forschung zum 1. Jahrtausend n. Chr.* (2022): 283–97, esp. 288–91.

7 Joscha Gretzinger, Duncan Sayer, Pierre Justeau, Eveline Altena, Maria Pala, Katharina Dulias, Ceiridwen J. Edwards et al., 'The Anglo-Saxon Migration and the Formation of the Early English Gene Pool', *Nature* 610, no. 7930 (October 2022): 112–19.

8 Ashot Margaryan, Daniel J. Lawson, Martin Sikora, Fernando Racimo, Simon Rasmussen, Ida Moltke, Lara M. Cassidy et al., 'Population Genomics of the Viking World', *Nature* 585, no. 7825 (September 2020): 390–6.

9 Ricardo Rodríguez-Varela, Kristjan H. S. Moore, S. Sunna Ebenesersdóttir, Gulsah Merve Kilinc, Anna Kjellström, Ludvig Papmehl-Dufay, Clara Alfsdotter et al., 'The Genetic History of Scandinavia from the Roman Iron Age to the Present', *Cell* 186, no. 1 (January 2023): 32–46.

10 Krishna R. Veeramah, Andreas Rott, Melanie Groß, Lucy Van Dorp, Saioa López, Karola Kirsanow, Christian Sell et al., 'Population Genomic Analysis of Elongated Skulls Reveals Extensive Female-Biased Immigration in Early Medieval Bavaria', *Proceedings of the National Academy of Sciences* 115, no. 13 (March 2018): 3494–9.

11 Jens Blöcher, Leonardo Vallini, Maren Velte, Raphael Eckel, Léa Guyon, Laura Winkelbach, Mark G. Thomas et al., 'Historic Genomes Uncover Demographic Shifts and Kinship Structures in Post-Roman Central Europe', Preprint, *Genetics*, 6 March 2025.

12 Walter Pohl, Johannes Krause, Tividar Vida and Patrick Geary, 'Integrating Genetic, Archaeological, and Historical Perspectives on Eastern Central Europe, 400–900 AD', *Historical Studies on Central Europe* 1, no. 1 (2021): 213–28.

13 Roland Steinacher, *Rom Und Die Barbaren: Völker im Alpen- und Donauraum (300–600)*, 1. Auflage (Stuttgart: Verlag W. Kohlhammer, 2017).

14 On the history of Pannonia in the Roman period, the fundamental works are Péter Kovács, *A History of Pannonia during the Principate*,

Antiquitas, Band 65 (Bonn: Dr. Rudolf Habelt, 2014); Péter Kovács, *A History of Pannonia in the Late Roman Period I (284–363 AD)*, Antiquitas, Reihe 1, Abhandlungen zur alten Geschichte, Band 67 (Bonn: Dr. Rudolf Habelt GmbH, 2016); and, for the primary sources, Péter Kovács, *Die antiken Quellen zu Pannonien in der Spätantike* (Vienna: Phoibos Verlag, 2014).

15 Jenő Fitz, 'Historical Outline of the Roman Period', in Zolt Visy, ed., *Hungarian Archaeology at the Turn of the Millennium*, 205–8 (Budapest: Ministry of National Cultural Heritage, Teleki László foundation, 2003).

16 Kovács, *Principate*, 75.

17 Dénes Gabler, 'Villas', in *Archaeology at the Turn of the Millennium*, 235–8, and Sylvia Palágyi, 'Roman Villas North of Lake Balaton', in *Archaeology at the Turn of the Millennium*, 238–41.

18 Dénes Gabler, 'Rural Settlements in Pannonia', in *Archaeology at the Turn of the Millennium*, 241–2.

19 Generally, Noel Lenski, *Failure of Empire: Valens and the Roman State in the Fourth Century A.D.* The Transformation of the Classical Heritage 34 (Berkeley: University of California Press, 2002), Chapter 1: 'The Pannonian Emperors', 14–67.

20 Tivadar Vida, ed., *The Frontier World: Romans, Barbarians and Military Culture*, vol. II, *Romania Gothica* (Budapest: Martin Optiz Kiadó, 2015).

21 On the transformation of the Pannonian countryside during the Migration period, see Tivadar Vida, 'The Migration-Period Countryside in the Former Roman Province of Pannonia', in Irene Bavuso and Angelo Castrorao Barba, eds, *The European Countryside during the Migration Period Patterns of Change from Iberia to the Caucasus (300–700 CE)*, 103–30 Ergänzungsbände zum Reallexikon der Germanischen Altertumskunde Volume 137 (Berlin: De Gruyter, 2023).

22 Deven N. Vyas, István Koncz, Alessandra Modi, Balázs Gusztáv Mende, Yijie Tian, Paolo Francalacci, Martina Lari et al., 'Fine-Scale Sampling Uncovers the Complexity of Migrations in 5th–6th Century Pannonia', *Current Biology* 33, no. 18 (September 2023).

23 Guido Alberto Gnecchi-Ruscone, Zsófia Rácz, Salvatore Liccardo, Juhyeon Lee, Yilei Huang, Luca Traverso, Rita Radzevičiūtė et al., 'Ancient Genomes Reveal Trans-Eurasian Connections between the European Huns and the Xiongnu Empire', *Proceedings of the National Academy of Sciences* 122, no. 9 (March 2025).

24 Herwig Wolfram, *History of the Goths* (Berkeley: University of California Press, 1988), 260–1.

25 Róbert Müller, 'The Romanized Population in the 5th–6th Centuries', in *Hungarian Archaeology at the Turn of the Millennium*, 289–91.

26 Margaret L. Antonio et al., 'Ancient Rome: A genetic crossroads of Europe and the Mediterranean', *Science* 366, no. 6466 (November 2019): 673.

27 Deven N. Vyas, István Koncz, Alessandra Modi et al., 'Fine-scale sampling uncovers the complexity of migrations in 5th–6th century Pannonia', *Current Biology* 33, no. 18 (25 September 2023): 3951–61.e11.

28 Blöcher et al., 'Historic Genomes Uncover Demographic Shifts'.

29 Yijie Tian, István Koncz, Norbert Faragó, Corina Knipper, Ronny Friedrich, Deven N. Vyas, Levente Samu et al., 'Unveiling the Complexity of Post-Roman Polity Formation Using Ancient DNA', Preprint, *Evolutionary Biology*, 19 August 2025.

30 Joscha Gretzinger, Felix Biermann, Hellen Mager, Benedict King, Denisa Zlámalová, Luca Traverso, Guido A. Gnecchi Ruscone et al., 'Ancient DNA Connects Large-Scale Migration with the Spread of Slavs', Preprint, *Nature*, 3 September 2025.

31 Velleius Paterculus, *Historia Romana*, II, 106.

32 Strabo, *Geography*, VII, 1,3.

33 Tacitus, *Annales*, XI, 17.

34 Tacitus, *Germania*, 40.

35 Cassius Dio, *Roman History*, LXXII.

36 Procopius, *De Bello Gothico*, II, 14.

37 Procopius, *History of the Wars*, VII, 33, 1.

38 On the history of the Avars, see Walter Pohl, *The Avars: A Steppe Empire in Central Europe, 567–822* (Ithaca, NY: Cornell University Press, 2018).

39 Hugh McColl, Guus Kroonen, J. Víctor Moreno-Mayar, Frederik Valeur Seersholm, Gabriele Scorrano, Thomaz Pinotti, Tharsika Vimala et al., 'Steppe Ancestry in Western Eurasia and the Spread of the Germanic Languages', Preprint, *Genetics*, 14 March 2024.

40 Amorim et al., 'Understanding 6th-Century Barbarian Social Organization'.

41 Kurt W. Alt, Corina Knipper, Daniel Peters, Wolfgang Müller, Anne-France Maurer, Isabelle Kollig, Nicole Nicklisch et al., 'Lombards on the Move – An Integrative Study of the Migration Period Cemetery at Szólád, Hungary', *PLoS ONE* 9, no. 11 (November 2014).

42 Tian et al., 'Unveiling the Complexity of Post-Roman Polity'.

43 Justin Favrod, *La Chronique de Marius d'Avenches (455–581) / Texte, Traduction et Commentaire* (Lausanne: Section d'histoire, Faculté des lettres, Université de Lausanne, 1991), 82.

44 On Alboin's decision to leave Pannonia to the Avars, see Pohl, *The Avars*, 62–8.

45 Paulus Diaconus, *History of the Lombards*, II, 7.

46 *Origo Gentis Langobardorum*, in Georg Waitz, ed., Monumenta Germaniae Historica, Scriptores rerum Langobardicarum et Italicarum saec. VI–XI, 5–6 (Hannover: Hahn 1868).

47 On Secundus of Non/Trent, whose work Paulus Diaconus used, see Walter Pohl, 'Paolo Diacono e la construzione dell'identità longobarda', in Paolo Chiesa, ed., *Paolo Diacono. Uno scrittore fra tra- dizione longobarda e rinnovamento carolingio*, 413–26. Convegno internazionale di studi, Cividale del Friuli–Udine, 6–9 Maggio 1999 (Turnhout, Belgium: Brepols, 2000); and Ken Gardiner, 'Paul the Deacon and Secundus of Trento', in Brian Croke and Alanna M. Emmett, eds, *History and Historians in Late Antiquity*, 147–53 (Sydney and New York: Pergamon Press, 1983).

48 Paulus Diaconus, *Historia Langobardorum*, II, 26.

49 *Edictus Rothari. in Edictus Ceteraeque Langobardorum Leges: Cum Constitutionibus et Pactis Principum Beneventanorum. Ex Maiore Editione Monumentis Germaniae inserta*, ed. Friedrich Bluhme (Hannover: Inpensis Bibliopolii Hahniani, 1869), 1–73.

50 Giorgio Ausenda, 'A Comparative Discussion of Langobardic Feud and Blood Money Compensation with Parallels from Contemporary Anthropology and from Medieval History', in *The Langobards before the Frankish Conquest: An Ethnographic Perspective*, 309–39, esp. 315–17 (Woodbridge: Boydell Press; Rochester, NY: San Marino, 2009).

51 Favrod, *La Chronique de Marius d'Avenches*, 82.

52 *Edictus Rothari*, 177.

53 Pauli, *Historia Langobardorum* II, 9: 'Faras, hoc est generationes vel lineas'.

54 The meaning of the term *fara* has long been debated. For an overview of earlier literature, see Alexander C. Murray, *Germanic Kinship Structure: Studies in Law and Society in Antiquity and in the Early Middle Ages* (Toronto: Pontifical Institute of Mediaeval Studies, 1983), chap. 5: 'The Fara', 89–97. Previous generations saw it as a vast agnatic or clan lineage, an argument drawn from Paul the Deacon's

definition of *fara* as *generationes vel lineas* (*Historia Langobard*orum II, 9, 78). Others, following Gian Piero Bognetti, 'L'influsso delle istituzioni militari romane sulle istituzioni longobarde del secolo VI e la natura della "fara"', in *L'età longobarda* (Milan: Giuffrè, 1966–8), t. 3, 1–46, consider the *fara* as a military unit during the migration period. Wolfgang Haubrichs has studied the etymology of *fara* in the context of political processes in '"Leudes, fara, faramanni und farone": Zur Semantik der Bezeichnungen für einige der am Konsenshandeln beteiligte Gruppen', in Verena Epp and Christoph H. F. Meyer, eds, *Recht und Konsens im frühen Mittelalter*, Vorträge und Forschungen, vol. 82, 235–63 (Ostfildern: Jan Thorbecke Verlag, 2017). On *fara*, see 248–63. Haubrichs argues that the original meaning of *fara* in west Germanic languages was 'something that is part of a journey, an excursion, an expedition, a migration'. He further argues that the meaning of the kinship association 'Family' is probably due to an extension arising from the temporary collapse of the kinship association and the itinerant community (249).

55 Yjie Tian, István Koncz, Sarah Defant, Caterina Giostra, Deven N. Vyas, Arkadiusz Sołtysiak, Luisella Pejrani Baricco et al., 'The Role of Emerging Elites in the Formation and Development of Communities after the Fall of the Roman Empire', *Proceedings of the National Academy of Sciences* 121, no. 36 (September 2024).

56 Tian, Konvz, Defant, 'The Role of Emerging Elites'.

57 István Koncz, '568 – A Historical Date and Its Archaeological Consequences', *Acta Archaeologica Academiae Scientiarum Hungaricae* 66 (2015): 315–40.

58 Lester K. Little, ed., *Plague and the End of Antiquity: The Pandemic of 541–750* (Cambridge: Cambridge University Press, 2007).

59 Peter Sarris, 'New Approaches to the "Plague of Justinian"', *Past and Present* 254 (2022): 315–46; Michael McCormick, 'Gregory of Tours on Sixth-Century Plague and Other Epidemics', *Speculum* 96 (2021): 38–96.

60 Kyle Harper, *The Fate of Rome: Climate, Disease, and the End of an Empire,* The Princeton History of the Ancient World (Princeton, NJ: Princeton University Press, 2017).

61 Lee Mordechai and Merle Eisenberg, 'Rejecting Catastrophe: The Case of the Justinianic Plague', *Past and Present* 244 (2019): 3–244, citation, 8. But see Micha Meier, 'The "Justinianic Plague" – Die "Justinianische Pest": An "Inconsequential Pandemic"? A Reply', *Medizinhistorisches Journal* 55, no. 2 (2020): 172–99; and the response: Lee Mordechai, Merle Eisenberg, Timothy Newfield, Adam Izdebski and Janet Kay, 'Quantitative Analysis and Plagued

Assumptions: A Response to Mischa Meier', *Medizinhistorisches Journal* 55, no. 3 (2020): 290–3.

62 Timothy P. Newfield, 'One Plague for Another? Interdisciplinary Shortcomings in Plague Studies and the Place of the Black Death in Histories of the Justinianic Plague', *Studies in Late Antiquity* 6, no. 4 (2022): 575–626; Timothy P. Newfield, Neil Roberts, Elena Xoplaki, Jürg Luterbacher, Inga Labuhn, Warren Eastwood, Hugh Elton, Dominik Fleitmann, Adam Izdebski and Arlene Rosen, 'Proxies for Plague? New Approaches in Studying the Causes and Consequences of the First Plague Pandemic', in W. Brandes, H. Reimitz and J. Tannous, eds, *Legal Pluralism and Social Change in Late Antiquity and the Middle Ages: A Conference in Honor of John Haldon*, 63–115 (Frankfurt: Klostermann, 2024).

63 Michael Feldman, Michaela Harbeck, Marcel Keller, Maria A. Spyrou, Andreas Rott, Bernd Trautmann, Holger C. Scholz et al., 'A High-Coverage Yersinia Pestis Genome from a Sixth-Century Justinianic Plague Victim', *Molecular Biology and Evolution* 33, no. 11 (November 2016): 2911–23.

64 Herbig et al., in preparation.

65 Pohl, *Avars*, 38–47.

66 Guido Alberto Gnecchi-Ruscone, Guido Alberto, Anna Szécsényi-Nagy, István Koncz, Gergely Csiky, Zsófia Rácz, A. B. Rohrlach, Guido Brandt et al., 'Ancient Genomes Reveal Origin and Rapid Trans-Eurasian Migration of 7th Century Avar Elites', *Cell* 185, no. 8 (April 2022).

67 Guido Alberto Gnecchi-Ruscone, Zsófia Rácz, Levente Samu, Tamás Szeniczey, Norbert Faragó, Corina Knipper, Ronny Friedrich et al., 'Network of Large Pedigrees Reveals Social Practices of Avar Communities', *Nature* 629, no. 8011 (May 2024): 376–83.

68 Ke Wang, Bendeguz Tobias, Doris Pany-Kucera, Margit Berner, Sabine Eggers, Guido Alberto Gnecchi-Ruscone, Denisa Zlámalová et al., 'Ancient DNA Reveals Reproductive Barrier Despite Shared Avar-Period Culture', Preprint, *Nature*, 15 January 2025.

69 Wang, Tobias, Pany-Kucera, et al., 'Ancient DNA Reveals Reproductive Barrier'.

70 Especially Florin Curta, *The Making of the Slavs: History and Archaeology of the Lower Danube Region, ca. 500–700*, Cambridge Studies in Medieval Life and Thought, 4th ser., 52 (Cambridge: Cambridge University Press, 2001).

71 Joscha Gretzinger, Felix Biermann, Hellen Mager, Benedict King, Denisa Zlámalová, Luca Traverso, Guido A. Gnecchi Ruscone et al.,

'Ancient DNA Connects Large-Scale Migration with the Spread of Slavs', Preprint, *Nature*, 3 September 2025.

72 Robert Nedoma, Petr Dresler, Ilektra Schulz, Elias Lagonik, Stephen M. Johnson, Ludmila Kaňáková et al., 'Runes from Lány (Czech Republic) – The Oldest Inscription among Slavs. A New Standard for Multidisciplinary Analysis of Runic Bones', *Journal of Archaeological Science* 127 (March 2021).

BIBLIOGRAPHY

1000 Genomes Project Consortium, Corresponding authors, Adam Auton, Gonçalo R. Abecasis, Steering committee, David M. Altshuler, Richard M. Durbin, et al. 'A Global Reference for Human Genetic Variation'. *Nature* 526, no. 7571 (October 2015): 68–74, https://doi.org/10.1038/nature15393.

Adler, Tal, Linda Fibiger, John Harris, Maria Teschler-Nicola, Joan Smith and Anna Szöke. 'Dead Images: Facing the history, ethics and politics of European skull collections'. In M. Hamm and K. Schönberger, eds, *Contentious Heritages and Arts: A Critical Companion*, 63–8. Klagenfurt: Wieser Verlag, 2012.

Alexander, David H., John Novembre and Kenneth Lange. 'Fast Model-Based Estimation of Ancestry in Unrelated Individuals'. *Genome Research* 19, no. 9 (September 2009): 1655–64, https://doi.org/10.1101/gr.094052.109.

Allentoft, Morten E., Martin Sikora, Karl-Göran Sjögren, Simon Rasmussen, Morten Rasmussen, Jesper Stenderup, Peter B. Damgaard et al. 'Population Genomics of Bronze Age Eurasia'. *Nature* 522, no. 7555 (June 2015): 167–72, https://doi.org/10.1038/nature14507.

Alt, Kurt W., Corina Knipper, Daniel Peters, Wolfgang Müller, Anne-France Maurer, Isabelle Kollig, Nicole Nicklisch et al. 'Lombards on the Move – An Integrative Study of the Migration Period Cemetery at Szólád, Hungary'. *PLoS ONE* 9, no. 11 (November 2014), e110793, https://doi.org/10.1371/journal.pone.0110793.

Ammerman, Albert J. and L. L. Cavalli-Sforza. *The Neolithic Transition and the Genetics of Populations in Europe*. Princeton, NJ: Princeton University Press, 1984.

Amorim, Carlos Eduardo G., Stefania Vai, Cosimo Posth, Alessandra Modi, István Koncz, Susanne Hakenbeck, Maria Cristina La Rocca et al. 'Understanding 6th-Century Barbarian Social Organization and Migration through Paleogenomics'. *Nature Communications* 9, no. 1 (September 2018): 3547, https://doi.org/10.1038/s41467-018-06024-4.

Antonio, Margaret L., Ziyue Gao, Hannah M. Moots, Michaela Lucci, Francesca Candilio, Susanna Sawyer, Victoria Oberreiter et al. 'Ancient Rome: A Genetic Crossroads of Europe and the Mediterranean'.

Science 366, no. 6466 (November 2019): 708–14, https://doi.org/10.1126/science.aay6826.

Antonio, Margaret L, Clemens L Weiß, Ziyue Gao, Susanna Sawyer, Victoria Oberreiter, Hannah M. Moots, Jeffrey P. Spence et al. 'Stable Population Structure in Europe since the Iron Age, despite High Mobility'. *eLife* 13 (January 2024): e79714, https://doi.org/10.7554/eLife.79714.

Ausenda, Giorgio. 'A Comparative Discussion of Langobardic Feud and Blood Money Compensation with Parallels from Contemporary Anthropology and from Medieval History'. In *The Langobards before the Frankish Conquest: An Ethnographic Perspective*, 309–39. Woodbridge and Rochester, NY: San Marino, Boydell Press, 2009.

Ausenda, Giorgio, Chris Wickham and Paolo Delogu, eds. *The Langobards before the Frankish Conquest: An Ethnographic Perspective*. Studies in Historical Archaeoethnology, vol. 8. Woodbridge and Rochester, NY: Boydell Press, 2009.

Bálint, Cs. 'Some Problems in Genetic Research on Hungarian Ethnogenesis'. *Acta Archaeologica Academiae Scientiarum Hungaricae* 61, no. 1 (June 2010): 283–94, https://doi.org/10.1556/AArch.61.2010.1.9.

Bavuso, Irene. *The European Countryside During the Migration Period: Patterns of Change from Iberia to the Caucasus (300–700 CE)*, 1st edn. With Angelo Castrorao Barba. Ergänzungsbände zum Reallexikon der Germanischen Altertumskunde Series, vol. 137. Berlin and Boston: Walter de Gruyter GmbH, 2023.

Beumann, Helmut and Werner Schröder, eds. *Frühmittelalterliche Ethnogenese im Alpenraum*. Nationes, Bd. 5. Sigmaringen: J. Thorbecke, 1985.

Blöcher, Jens, Leonardo Vallini, Maren Velte, Raphael Eckel, Léa Guyon, Laura Winkelbach, Mark G. Thomas et al. 'Historic Genomes Uncover Demographic Shifts and Kinship Structures in Post-Roman Central Europe'. Preprint, *Genetics*, 6 March 2025, https://doi.org/10.1101/2025.03.01.640862.

Bognetti, Gian Piero. *L'età longobarda*, 4 vols. Milan: Giuffrè, 1966.

Borgolte, Michael. 'Migrationen als transkulturelle Verflechtungen im Mittelalterlichen Europa. Ein neuer Pflug für alte Forschungsfelder' (Migrations as Cross-Cultural Interactions in Medieval Europe. A New Plough for Old Research Fields). *Historische Zeitschrift* 289, no. 2 (January 2009), https://doi.org/10.1524/hzhz.2009.0041.

Borgolte, Michael. 'Mythos Völkerwanderung: Migration oder Expansion bei den "Ursprüngen Europas"'. *Viator (English and Multilingual Edition)* 41 (January 2010): 23–47, https://doi.org/10.1484/J.VIATOR.1.100725.

Bösl, Elsbeth. *Doing Ancient DNA: Zur Wissenschaftsgeschichte der aDNA-Forschung*. 1st edn. Histoire 111. Bielefeld: Transcript Verlag, 2017.

Bösl, Elsbeth, and Jörg Feuchter. 'Genetic History – Eine Herausforderung für die Geschichtswissenschaften'. *Neue Politische Literatur* 64, no. 2 (July 2019): 237–68, https://doi.org/10.1007/s42520-019-00111-6.

Brandes, Wolfram, Helmut Reimitz and Jack Tannous, eds. *Legal Pluralism and Social Change in Late Antiquity and the Middle Ages: A Conference in Honor of John Haldon*. Klostermann, 2024, https://doi.org/10.5771/9783465145509.

Brather, Sebastian. 'Ethnische Identitäten als Konstrukte der Frühgeschichtlichen Archäologie'. *Germania* 78, no. 1 (2000): 139–77.

Brather, Sebastian. *Archäologie der westlichen Slawen: Siedlung, Wirtschaft und Gesellschaft im früh- und hochmittelalterlichen Ostmitteleuropa*. Ergänzungsbände zum Reallexikon der Germanischen Altertumskunde, Bd. 30. Berlin and New York: De Gruyter, 2001.

Browning, Sharon R. and Brian L. Browning. 'Accurate Non-Parametric Estimation of Recent Effective Population Size from Segments of Identity by Descent'. *American Journal of Human Genetics* 97, no. 3 (September 2015): 404–18, https://doi.org/10.1016/j.ajhg.2015.07.012.

Cary, Ernest, trans. *Dio's Roman History*. 9 vols. Loeb Classical Library. London: Heinemann, 1914.

Cavalli-Sforza, Luigi L. *Genes, Peoples, and Languages*. 2nd edn. New York: North Point Press, 2000.

Chiesa, Paolo. *Paolo Diacono: uno scrittore fra tradizione longobarda e rinnovamento carolingio atti del convegno internazionale di studi, Cividale del Friuli, Udine, 6–9 maggio 1999*. Associazione per gli studi storici e artistici di Cividale, Università di Udine. Libri e biblioteche 9. Udine: Forum, 2000.

Cooper, Alan and Hendrik N. Poinar. 'Ancient DNA: Do It Right or Not at All'. *Science* 289, no. 5482 (August 2000): 1139, https://doi.org/10.1126/science.289.5482.1139b.

Croke, Brian and Alanna M. Emmett, eds. *History and Historians in Late Antiquity*. Sydney and New York: Pergamon Press, 1983.

Curta, Florin. *The Making of the Slavs: History and Archaeology of the Lower Danube Region, ca. 500–700*. Cambridge Studies in Medieval Life and Thought, 4th ser., 52. Cambridge: Cambridge University Press, 2001, https://doi.org/10.1017/CBO9780511496295.

Curta, Florin. 'From Kossinna to Bromley: Ethnogenesis in Slavic Archaeology'. In Andrew Gillett, ed., *On Barbarian Identity: Critical Approaches to Ethnicity in the Early Middle Ages*, 201–18. Turnhout: Brepols, 2002.

De Craecker-Dussart, Christiane. 'Un "hommage" à Georges Duby'. *Le Moyen Age* 103, no. 3 (1997): 571, https://doi.org/10.3917/rma.033.0571.

Edictus Rothari, in *Edictus Ceteraeque Langobardorum Leges: Cum Constitutionibus et Pactis Principum Beneventanorum. Ex Maiore Editione Monumentis Germaniae inserta*, ed. Friedrich Bluhme, 1–73. Hannover: Inpensis Bibliopolii Hahniani, 1869.

Edwards, A. W. F. and L. L. Cavalli-Sforza. 'Reconstruction of Evolutionary Trees'. In V. H. Heywood and John McNeill, eds, *Phenetic and Phylogenetic Classification*, 67–76 Systematics Association Publications 6. London: Systematics Association, 1964.

Eisenmann, Stefanie, Eszter Bánffy, Peter Van Dommelen, Kerstin P. Hofmann, Joseph Maran, Iosif Lazaridis, Alissa Mittnik et al. 'Reconciling Material Cultures in Archaeology with Genetic Data: The Nomenclature of Clusters Emerging from Archaeogenomic Analysis'. *Scientific Reports* 8, no. 1 (August 2018): 13003, https://doi.org/10.1038/s41598-018-31123-z.

Esposito, Umberto, Ranajit Das, Syakir Syed, Mehdi Pirooznia and Eran Elhaik. 'Ancient Ancestry Informative Markers for Identifying Fine-Scale Ancient Population Structure in Eurasians'. *Genes* 9, no. 12 (December 2018): 625, https://doi.org/10.3390/genes9120625.

Fabian, Ann. *The Skull Collectors: Race, Science, and America's Unburied Dead*. Chicago: University of Chicago Press, 2010.

Favrod, Justin. *La Chronique de Marius d'Avenches (455–581): Texte, Traduction et Commentaire*. Lausanne: Section d'histoire, Faculté des lettres, Université de Lausanne, 1991.

Febvre, Lucien. *Combats pour l'histoire*. Paris: A. Colin, 1953.

Feldman, Michal, Michaela Harbeck, Marcel Keller, Maria A. Spyrou, Andreas Rott, Bernd Trautmann, Holger C. Scholz et al. 'A High-Coverage *Yersinia Pestis* Genome from a Sixth-Century Justinianic Plague Victim'. *Molecular Biology and Evolution* 33, no. 11 (November 2016): 2911–23, https://doi.org/10.1093/molbev/msw170.

Feuchter, Jörg. 'Für einen kritischen Dialog zwischen Geschichtswissenschaft und Genetic History'. *NTM Zeitschrift für Geschichte der Wissenschaften, Technik und Medizin* 26 (2018): 339–44.

Feuchter, Jörg. 'The Middle Ages in the Genetics Lab'. In Chris Jones, Conor Kostick and Klaus Oschema, eds, *Making the Medieval Relevant*, 99–112. Berlin and Boston: De Gruyter, 2019. https://doi.org/10.1515/9783110546316-004.

Fitz, Jenő. 'Historical Outline of the Roman Period'. In Zsolt Visy, ed., *Hungarian Archaeology at the Turn of the Millennium*, 205–8. Budapest: Ministry of National Cultural Heritage, Teleki László foundation, 2003.

'Forum: Genetic History'. *NTM Zeitschrift für Geschichte der Wissenschaften, Technik und Medizin* 26, no. 3 (September 2018): 301–50, https://doi.org/10.1007/s00048-018-0196-9.
Foster, Eugene A., M. A. Jobling, P. G. Taylor, P. Donnelly, P. De Knijff, R. Mieremet, T. Zerjal, and C. Tyler-Smith. 'Jefferson Fathered Slave's Last Child'. *Nature* 396, no. 6706 (November 1998): 27–8, https://doi.org/10.1038/23835.
Foster, Eugene. A., M. A. Jobling, P. G. Taylor, P. Donnelly, P. De Knijff, R. Mieremet, T. Zerjal, and C. Tyler-Smith. 'Reply: The Thomas Jefferson Paternity Case'. *Nature* 397, no. 6714 (January 1999): 32, https://doi.org/10.1038/16181.
Furtwängler, Anja, A. B. Rohrlach, Thiseas C. Lamnidis, Luka Papac, Gunnar U. Neumann, Inga Siebke, Ella Reiter et al. 'Ancient Genomes Reveal Social and Genetic Structure of Late Neolithic Switzerland'. *Nature Communications* 11, no. 1 (April 2020): 1915, https://doi.org/10.1038/s41467-020-15560-x.
Gabler, Dénes. 'Rural Settlements in Pannonia'. In *Hungarian Archaeology at the Turn of the Millennium*, 241–2. Budapest: Ministry of National Cultural Heritage, Teleki László foundation, 2003.
Gabler, Dénes. 'Villas'. In *Hungarian Archaeology at the Turn of the Millennium*, 235–8. Budapest: Ministry of National Cultural Heritage, Teleki László foundation, 2003.
Gannon, Megan. 'When Ancient DNA Gets Politicized'. *Smithsonian Magazine*, 12 July 2019, https://www.smithsonianmag.com/history/when-ancient-dna-gets-politicized-180972639/.
Gardiner, Ken. 'Paul the Deacon and Secundus of Trento'. In *History and Historians in Late Antiquity*, 147–53. Sydney and New York: Pergamon Press, 1983.
Geary, Patrick J. *The Myth of Nations: The Medieval Origins of Europe*. Princeton, NJ: Princeton University Press, 2002.
Geary, Patrick J. 'La Femme de la Tombe 087 à Collegno: La Paléogénomique au service de l'histoire d'une communauté en Italie lombarde'. *Mémoires de la Société nationale des antiquaires de France*, in press.
Geary, Patrick and Krishna Veeramah. 'Mapping European Population Movement through Genomic Research'. *Medieval Worlds*, 2016, no. 4 (2016): 65–78, https://doi.org/10.1553/medievalworlds_no4_2016s65.
Gillett, Andrew, ed. *On Barbarian Identity: Critical Approaches to Ethnicity in the Early Middle Ages*. Studies in the Early Middle Ages, vol. 4. International Congress on Medieval Studies. Turnhout, Belgium: Brepols, 2002.
Gnecchi-Ruscone, Guido Alberto, Zsófia Rácz, Salvatore Liccardo, Juhyeon Lee, Yilei Huang, Luca Traverso, Rita Radzevičiūtė et al.

'Ancient Genomes Reveal Trans-Eurasian Connections between the European Huns and the Xiongnu Empire'. *Proceedings of the National Academy of Sciences* 122, no. 9 (March 2025): e2418485122, https://doi.org/10.1073/pnas.2418485122.

Gnecchi-Ruscone, Guido Alberto, Zsófia Rácz, Levente Samu, Tamás Szeniczey, Norbert Faragó, Corina Knipper, Ronny Friedrich et al. 'Network of Large Pedigrees Reveals Social Practices of Avar Communities'. *Nature* 629, no. 8011 (May 2024): 376–83, https://doi.org/10.1038/s41586-024-07312-4.

Gnecchi-Ruscone, Guido Alberto, Anna Szécsényi-Nagy, István Koncz, Gergely Csiky, Zsófia Rácz, A. B. Rohrlach, Guido Brandt et al. 'Ancient Genomes Reveal Origin and Rapid Trans-Eurasian Migration of 7th Century Avar Elites'. *Cell* 185, no. 8 (April 2022): 1402–13. e21, https://doi.org/10.1016/j.cell.2022.03.007.

Gobineau, Arthur de. *Essai sur l'inégalité des races humaines*, 4 vols. Paris: Imprimerie de Firmin Didot frères, 1853.

Goold, George P. and H. B. Dewing, trans. *Procopius: History of the Wars*, 5 vols. Loeb Classical Library. Cambridge, MA: Harvard University Press, 1914.

Gramsch, Alexander. 'Culture, Change, Identity. Approaches to the Interpretation of Cultural Change'. *Anthropologie* 53, no. 3 (2015): 341–9.

Gretzinger, Joscha, Felix Biermann, Hellen Mager, Benedict King, Denisa Zlámalová, Luca Traverso, Guido A. Gnecchi Ruscone et al. 'Ancient DNA Connects Large-Scale Migration with the Spread of Slavs'. *Nature* 646, no. 8084 (September 2025): 384–93, https://doi.org/10.1038/s41586-025-09437-6.

Gretzinger, Joscha, Duncan Sayer, Pierre Justeau, Eveline Altena, Maria Pala, Katharina Dulias, Ceiridwen J. Edwards et al. 'The Anglo-Saxon Migration and the Formation of the Early English Gene Pool'. *Nature* 610, no. 7930 (October 2022): 112–19, https://doi.org/10.1038/s41586-022-05247-2.

Gretzinger, Joscha and Stephan Schiffels. 'A Glimpse into Darkness: Population Genetics of the European Middle Ages'. In *New Narratives for the First Millennium* AD*?: Alte und neue Perspektiven der archäologischen Forschung zum 1. Jahrtausend n. Chr.*, 283–97. Wendeburg: Uwe Krebs, 2022, https://doi.org/10.24355/DBBS.084-202301131414-0.

Haak, Wolfgang, Iosif Lazaridis, Nick Patterson, Nadin Rohland, Swapan Mallick, Bastien Llamas, Guido Brandt et al. 'Massive Migration from the Steppe Was a Source for Indo-European Languages in Europe'. *Nature* 522, no. 7555 (June 2015): 207–11, https://doi.org/10.1038/nature14317.

Hakenbeck, Susanne E. 'Genetics, Archaeology and the Far Right: An Unholy Trinity'. *World Archaeology* 51, no. 4 (August 2019): 517–27, https://doi.org/10.1080/00438243.2019.1617189.

Hallast, Pille, Anastasia Agdzhoyan, Oleg Balanovsky, Yali Xue and Chris Tyler-Smith. 'A Southeast Asian Origin for Present-Day Non-African Human Y Chromosomes'. *Human Genetics* 140, no. 2 (February 2021): 299–307, https://doi.org/10.1007/s00439-020-02204-9.

Halsall, Guy. 'Review Article: Movers and Shakers: The Barbarians and the Fall of Rome'. *Early Medieval Europe* 8, no. 1 (March 1999): 131–45, https://doi.org/10.1111/1468-0254.00041.

Halsall, Guy. 'Archaeology and the Late Roman Frontier in Northern Gaul: The So-Called Föderatengräber Reconsidered'. In Walter Pohl and Helmut Reimitz, eds, *Grenze und Differenz im frühen Mittelalter*, 167–80. Denkschriften/Österreichische Akademie der Wissenschaften, Philosophisch-Historische Klasse; Forschungen zur Geschichte des Mittelalters, 287. Bd. 1. Vienna: Verlag der Österreichischen Akademie der Wissenschaften, 2000.

Halsall, Guy. *Barbarian Migrations and the Roman West, 376–568.* Cambridge Medieval Textbooks. Cambridge: Cambridge University Press, 2007.

Hamm, Marion and Klaus Schönberger, eds. *Contentious Cultural Heritages and Arts: A Critical Companion.* Klagenfurt: Wieser Verlag, 2021.

Hansen, Henrik B., Peter B. Damgaard, Ashot Margaryan, Jesper Stenderup, Niels Lynnerup, Eske Willerslev and Morten E. Allentoft. 'Comparing Ancient DNA Preservation in Petrous Bone and Tooth Cementum'. *PLOS ONE* 12, no. 1 (January 2017): e0170940, https://doi.org/10.1371/journal.pone.0170940.

Harper, Kyle. *The Fate of Rome: Climate, Disease, and the End of an Empire.* The Princeton History of the Ancient World. Princeton, NJ: Princeton University Press, 2017.

Harris, David R., ed. *The Archaeology of V. Gordon Childe: Contemporary Perspectives.* London: University College London, 1994.

Haubrichs, Wolfgang. '"Leudes, fara, faramanni und farones": Zur Semantik der Bezeichnungen für einige am Konsenshandeln beteiligte Gruppen'. *Vorträge und Forschungen*, 10 March 2020, 235–63, https://doi.org/10.11588/VUF.2017.0.71813.

Heyd, Volker. 'Kossinna's Smile'. *Antiquity* 91, no. 356 (April 2017): 348–59, https://doi.org/10.15184/aqy.2017.21.

Heywood, V. H. and J. McNeill, eds. *Phenetic and Phylogenetic Classification*, vol. 6. London: Systematics Association, 1964.

Higuchi, Russell, Barbara Bowman, Mary Freiberger, Oliver A. Ryder and Allan C. Wilson. 'DNA Sequences from the Quagga, an Extinct

Member of the Horse Family'. *Nature* 312, no. 5991 (November 1984): 282–4, https://doi.org/10.1038/312282a0.

Ibrahim, Jamal, Vlad Brumfeld, Yoseph Addadi, Sarah Rubin, Steve Weiner and Elisabetta Boaretto. 'The Petrous Bone Contains High Concentrations of Osteocytes: One Possible Reason Why Ancient DNA Is Better Preserved in This Bone'. *PLOS ONE* 17, no. 10 (October 2022): e0269348, https://doi.org/10.1371/journal.pone.0269348.

Internullo, Dario. 'Du papyrus au parchemin: Les origines médiévales de la mémoire archivistique en Europe occidentale'. *Annales. Histoire, Sciences Sociales* 74, nos 3–4 (September 2019): 523–57, https://doi.org/10.1017/ahss.2020.52.

Jackson, John, trans. *Tacitus Works*, 5 vols. Loeb Classical Library. Cambridge, MA: Harvard University Press, 1960.

Jones, Elizabeth D. *Ancient DNA: The Making of a Celebrity Science.* New Haven, CT, and London: Yale University Press, 2022.

Jones, Horace Leonard, trans. *The Geography of Strabo*, 8 vols. Loeb Classical Library. Cambridge, MA: Harvard University Press, 1959.

Källén, Anna. *The Trouble with Ancient DNA: Telling Stories of the Past with Genomic Science.* Chicago: University of Chicago Press, 2025.

King, Turi E., Gloria Gonzalez Fortes, Patricia Balaresque, Mark G. Thomas, David Balding, Pierpaolo Maisano Delser, Rita Neumann et al. 'Identification of the Remains of King Richard III'. *Nature Communications* 5, no. 1 (December 2014): 5631, https://doi.org/10.1038/ncomms6631.

Koncz, István. '568 – A Historical Date and Its Archaeological Consequences'. *Acta Archaeologica Academiae Scientiarum Hungaricae* 66, no. 2 (2015): 315–40, https://doi.org/10.1556/072.2015.66.2.4.

Kossinna, Gustaf. *Die Deutsche Vorgeschichte: Eine Hervorragend nationale Wissenschaft.* Leipzig: C. Kabitzsch, 1912.

Kossinna, Gustaf. *Ursprung und Verbreitung der Germanen in vor-und Frühgeschichtlicher Zeit.* Leipzig: Mannus-Bibliothek, 1928.

Kovács, Péter. *Die antiken Quellen zu Pannonien in der Spätantike.* Vienna: Phoibos Verlag, 2014.

Kovács, Péter. *A History of Pannonia during the Principate.* Antiquitas, Band 65. Bonn: Dr. Rudolf Habelt, 2014.

Kovács, Péter. *A History of Pannonia in the Late Roman Period I (284–363 AD).* Antiquitas. Reihe 1, Abhandlungen zur alten Geschichte, Band 67. Bonn: Dr. Rudolf Habelt GmbH, 2016.

Kozłowski, Leon. *Epoka kamienia na wydmach wschodniej części Wyżyny Małopolskiej.* Lwów: Książnica polska, 1923.

Krause, Johannes and Thomas Trappe. *Hybris: die Reise der Menschheit: zwischen Aufbruch und Scheitern.* 4. Aufl. Berlin: Propyläen, 2021.

Lamm, Ehud, Oren Harman and Sophie Juliane Veigl. 'Before Watson and Crick in 1953 Came Friedrich Miescher in 1869'. *Genetics* 215, no. 2 (June 2020): 291–6, https://doi.org/10.1534/genetics.120.303195.

Langlois, Charles Victor and Charles Seignobos. *Introduction aux études historiques*. Paris: Hachette, 1898.

Lazaridis, Iosif, Nick Patterson, Alissa Mittnik, Gabriel Renaud, Swapan Mallick, Karola Kirsanow, Peter H. Sudmant et al. 'Ancient Human Genomes Suggest Three Ancestral Populations for Present-Day Europeans'. *Nature* 513, no. 7518 (September 2014): 409–13, https://doi.org/10.1038/nature13673.

Le, Megan K., Olivia S. Smith, Ali Akbari, Arbel Harpak, David Reich and Vagheesh M. Narasimhan. '1,000 Ancient Genomes Uncover 10,000 Years of Natural Selection in Europe'. Preprint, *Genomics*, 26 August 2022, https://doi.org/10.1101/2022.08.24.505188.

Lenski, Noel. *Failure of Empire: Valens and the Roman State in the Fourth Century A.D.* The Transformation of the Classical Heritage 34. Berkeley: University of California Press, 2002.

Lever, Jake, Martin Krzywinski and Naomi Altman. 'Principal Component Analysis'. *Nature Methods* 14, no. 7 (July 2017): 641–2, https://doi.org/10.1038/nmeth.4346.

Linnaei, Caroli. *Systema Naturae, sive regna tria naturae systematice proposita per classes, ordines, genera, & species*. Leiden: Theodorum Haak, 1735.

Lipatov, Mikhail, Komal Sanjeev, Rob Patro and Krishna R. Veeramah. 'Maximum Likelihood Estimation of Biological Relatedness from Low Coverage Sequencing Data'. Preprint, 29 July 2015, https://doi.org/10.1101/023374.

Lipson, Mark. 'Interpreting F-Statistics and Admixture Graphs: Theory and Examples'. Preprint, 15 March 2020, https://doi.org/10.20944/preprints202003.0237.v1.

Little, Lester K., ed. *Plague and the End of Antiquity: The Pandemic of 541–750*. New York: Cambridge University Press, 2007.

Loh, Po-Ru, Mark Lipson, Nick Patterson, Priya Moorjani, Joseph K. Pickrell, David Reich and Bonnie Berger. 'Inferring Admixture Histories of Human Populations Using Linkage Disequilibrium'. *Genetics* 193, no. 4 (April 2013): 1233–54, https://doi.org/10.1534/genetics.112.147330.

Lu, Clara, Rabeeyah Ahmed, Amel Lamri and Sonia S. Anand. 'Use of Race, Ethnicity, and Ancestry Data in Health Research'. *PLOS Global Public Health* 2, no. 9 (September 2022): e0001060, https://doi.org/10.1371/journal.pgph.0001060.

Maas, Michael. *The Conqueror's Gift: Roman Ethnography and the End of Antiquity*. Princeton, NJ: Princeton University Press, 2025.

Macháček, Jiří, Robert Nedoma, Petr Dresler, Ilektra Schulz, Elias Lagonik, Stephen M. Johnson, Ludmila Kaňáková et al. 'Runes from Lány (Czech Republic) – The Oldest Inscription among Slavs. A New Standard for Multidisciplinary Analysis of Runic Bones'. *Journal of Archaeological Science* 127 (March 2021): 105333, https://doi.org/10.1016/j.jas.2021.105333.

Mallick, Swapan, Heng Li, Mark Lipson, Iain Mathieson, Melissa Gymrek, Fernando Racimo, Mengyao Zhao et al. 'The Simons Genome Diversity Project: 300 Genomes from 142 Diverse Populations'. *Nature* 538, no. 7624 (October 2016): 201–6, https://doi.org/10.1038/nature18964.

Maples, Brian K., Simon Gravel, Eimear E. Kenny and Carlos D. Bustamante. 'RFMix: A Discriminative Modeling Approach for Rapid and Robust Local-Ancestry Inference'. *American Journal of Human Genetics* 93, no. 2 (August 2013): 278–88, https://doi.org/10.1016/j.ajhg.2013.06.020.

Margaryan, Ashot, Daniel J. Lawson, Martin Sikora, Fernando Racimo, Simon Rasmussen, Ida Moltke, Lara M. Cassidy et al. 'Population Genomics of the Viking World'. *Nature* 585, no. 7825 (September 2020): 390–6, https://doi.org/10.1038/s41586-020-2688-8.

McColl, Hugh, Guus Kroonen, J. Víctor Moreno-Mayar, Frederik Valeur Seersholm, Gabriele Scorrano, Thomaz Pinotti, Tharsika Vimala et al. 'Steppe Ancestry in Western Eurasia and the Spread of the Germanic Languages', Preprint, *Genetics*, 14 March 2024, https://doi.org/10.1101/2024.03.13.584607.

McCormick, Michael. 'Gregory of Tours on Sixth-Century Plague and Other Epidemics'. *Speculum* 96, no. 1 (2021): 38–96, https://doi.org/10.1086/711721.

McMahon, Richard. *The Races of Europe: Construction of National Identities in the Social Sciences, 1839–1939*. London: Palgrave Macmillan, 2016.

Meier, Mischa. 'The "Justinianic Plague": An "Inconsequential Pandemic"? A Reply'. *Medizinhistorisches Journal* 55, no. 2 (2020): 172, https://doi.org/10.25162/mhj-2020-0006.

Meier, Mischa. *Geschichte der Völkerwanderung: Europa, Asien und Afrika vom 3. bis zum 8. Jahrhundert n. Chr.* 7. Auflage. Historische Bibliothek der Gerda Henkel Stiftung. Munich: C.H. Beck, 2021.

Meier, Mischa and Steffen Patzold. *Gene und Geschichte: was die Archäogenetik zur Geschichtsforschung beitragen kann*. Zeitenspiegel Essay. Stuttgart: Anton Hiersemann KG, 2021.

Menozzi, P., A. Piazza and L. Cavalli-Sforza. 'Synthetic Maps of Human Gene Frequencies in Europeans: These Maps Indicate that Early Farmers of the Near East Spread to All of Europe in the Neolithic'.

Science 201, no. 4358 (September 1978): 786–92, https://doi.org/10.1126/science.356262.

Monroy Kuhn, Jose Manuel, Mattias Jakobsson and Torsten Günther. 'Estimating Genetic Kin Relationships in Prehistoric Populations'. *PLOS ONE* 13, no. 4 (April 2018): e0195491, https://doi.org/10.1371/journal.pone.0195491.

Moorjani, Priya, Sriram Sankararaman, Qiaomei Fu, Molly Przeworski, Nick Patterson and David Reich. 'A Genetic Method for Dating Ancient Genomes Provides a Direct Estimate of Human Generation Interval in the Last 45,000 Years'. *Proceedings of the National Academy of Sciences* 113, no. 20 (May 2016): 5652–7, https://doi.org/10.1073/pnas.1514696113.

Mordechai, Lee and Merle Eisenberg. 'Rejecting Catastrophe: The Case of the Justinianic Plague'. *Past & Present* 244, no. 1 (2019): 3–50, https://doi.org/10.1093/pastj/gtz009.

Mordechai, Lee, Merle Eisenberg, Timothy Newfield, Adam Izdebski and Janet Kay. 'Quantitative Analysis and Plagued Assumptions: A Response to Mischa Meier'. *Medizinhistorisches Journal* 55, no. 3 (2020): 290–3, https://doi.org/10.25162/mhj-2020-0011.

Morrison, Maike L., Nicolas Alcala and Noah A. Rosenberg. 'FSTRUCT : An FST-based Tool for Measuring Ancestry Variation in Inference of Population Structure'. *Molecular Ecology Resources* 22, no. 7 (October 2022): 2614–26, https://doi.org/10.1111/1755-0998.13647.

Müller. Róbert. 'The Romanized Population in the 5th–6th Centuries'. In *Hungarian Archaeology at the Turn of the Millennium*, 289–91. Budapest: Ministry of National Cultural Heritage Teleki László foundation, 2003.

Murray, Alexander C. *Germanic Kinship Structure: Studies in Law and Society in Antiquity and in the Early Middle Ages*. Toronto: Pontifical Institute of Mediaeval Studies, 1983.

Navarro-López, B., E. Granizo-Rodríguez, L. Palencia-Madrid, C. Raffone, M. Baeta and M. M. De Pancorbo. 'Phylogeographic Review of Y Chromosome Haplogroups in Europe'. *International Journal of Legal Medicine* 135, no. 5 (September 2021): 1675–84, https://doi.org/10.1007/s00414-021-02644-6.

Nelson, Matthew R., Katarzyna Bryc, Karen S. King, Amit Indap, Adam R. Boyko, John Novembre, Linda P. Briley et al. 'The Population Reference Sample, POPRES: A Resource for Population, Disease, and Pharmacological Genetics Research'. *American Journal of Human Genetics* 83, no. 3 (September 2008): 347–58, https://doi.org/10.1016/j.ajhg.2008.08.005.

Newfield, Timothy P. 'One Plague for Another? Interdisciplinary Shortcomings in Plague Studies and the Place of the Black Death in

Histories of the Justinianic Plague'. *Studies in Late Antiquity* 6, no. 4 (November 2022): 575–626, https://doi.org/10.1525/sla.2022.6.4.575.

Newfield, Timothy P., Neil Roberts, Elena Xoplaki, Jürg Luterbacher, Inga Labuhn, Warren Eastwood, Hugh Elton, Dominik Fleitmann, Adam Izdebski and Arlene Rosen. 'Proxies for Plague? New Approaches in Studying the Causes and Consequences of the First Plague Pandemic'. In W. Brandes, H. Reimitz and J. Tannous, eds, *Legal Pluralism and Social Change in Late Antiquity and the Middle Ages: A Conference in Honor of John Haldon*, 63–115. Frankfurt: Klostermann, 2024.

Nippel, Wilfried. *Griechen, Barbaren und 'Wilde': Alte Geschichte und Sozialanthropologie*. Originalausg. Geschichte Fischer. Frankfurt am Main: Fischer, 1990.

Novembre, John, Toby Johnson, Katarzyna Bryc, Zoltán Kutalik, Adam R. Boyko, Adam Auton, Amit Indap et al. 'Genes Mirror Geography within Europe'. *Nature* 456, no. 7218 (November 2008): 98–101, https://doi.org/10.1038/nature07331.

Olalde, Iñigo, Pablo Carrión, Ilija Mikić, Nadin Rohland, Swapan Mallick, Iosif Lazaridis, Matthew Mah et al. 'A Genetic History of the Balkans from Roman Frontier to Slavic Migrations'. *Cell* 186, no. 25 (December 2023): 5472–85.e9, https://doi.org/10.1016/j.cell.2023.10.018.

Olalde, Iñigo, Swapan Mallick, Nick Patterson, Nadin Rohland, Vanessa Villalba-Mouco, Marina Silva, Katharina Dulias et al. 'The Genomic History of the Iberian Peninsula over the Past 8000 Years'. *Science* 363, no. 6432 (March 2019): 1230–4, https://doi.org/10.1126/science.aav4040.

Origo Gentis Langobardorum, ed. Georg Waitz, Scriptores Rerum Langobardicarum et Italicarum Saec. VI–XI. Monumenta Germaniae Historica. Hannover: Hahn, 1868.

Osborne, Robin. *The History Written on the Classical Greek Body*. Cambridge: Cambridge University Press, 2011.

Palágyi, Sylvia. 'Roman Villas North of Lake Balaton'. In *Hungarian Archaeology at the Turn of the Millennium*, 205–8. Budapest: Ministry of National Cultural Heritage, Teleki László foundation, 2003.

Patterson, Nick, Priya Moorjani, Yontao Luo, Swapan Mallick, Nadin Rohland, Yiping Zhan, Teri Genschoreck, Teresa Webster and David Reich. 'Ancient Admixture in Human History'. *Genetics* 192, no. 3 (November 2012): 1065–93, https://doi.org/10.1534/genetics.112.145037.

Patterson, Nick, Alkes L. Price and David Reich. 'Population Structure and Eigenanalysis'. *PLoS Genetics* 2, no. 12 (2006): e190, https://doi.org/10.1371/journal.pgen.0020190.

Paulus. *Pauli Historia Langobardorum: in usum scholarum ex Monumentis Germaniae Historicis recusa*. Unveränd. Nachdr. der

Ausg. von 1878. Monumenta Germaniae Historica [Scriptores] Scriptores rerum Germanicarum in usum scholarum separatim editi 48. Hannover: Hahn, 2005.

Pinhasi, Ron, Daniel Fernandes, Kendra Sirak, Mario Novak, Sarah Connell, Songül Alpaslan-Roodenberg, Fokke Gerritsen et al. 'Optimal Ancient DNA Yields from the Inner Ear Part of the Human Petrous Bone'. *PLOS ONE* 10, no. 6 (June 2015): e0129102, https://doi.org/10.1371/journal.pone.0129102.

Pinkerton, John. *A Dissertation on the Origin and Progress of the Scythians or Goths, Being an Introduction to the Ancient and Modern History of Europe*. London: John Nichols, for George Nicol, Pall-Mall, 1787.

Pohl, Walter. *Die Awaren: Ein Steppenvolk in Mitteleuropa, 567–822 n. Chr*. Reihe 'Frühe Völker.' Munich: Beck, 1988.

Pohl, Walter. 'Conceptions of Ethnicity in Early Medieval Studies'. *Archaeologia Polona* 29 (1991): 39–49.

Pohl, Walter. 'Telling the Difference: Signs of Ethnic Identity'. In Walter Pohl and Helmut Reimitz, eds, *Strategies of Distinction: The Construction of Ethnic Communities, 300–800*, 17–69. Leiden: Brill, 1998.

Pohl, Walter. 'Paolo Diacono e la costruzione dell'identità longobarda'. In *Paolo Diacono: Uno scrittore fra tradizione longobarda e rinnovamento carolingio: Atti del convegno internazionale di studi: Cividale del Friuli-Udine, 6–9 Maggio 1999*, 413–26. Udine: Forum, 2000.

Pohl, Walter. 'Ethnicity, Theory and Tradition: A Response'. In Andrew Gillett, ed., *On Barbarian Identity: Critical Approaches to Ethnicity in the Early Middle Ages*, 122–239. Turnhout, Belgium: Brepols, 2002.

Pohl, Walter. *The Avars: A Steppe Empire in Central Europe, 567–822*. Ithaca, NY, and London: Cornell University Press, 2018.

Pohl, Walter, ed. *Kingdoms of the Empire: The Integration of Barbarians in Late Antiquity*. The Transformation of the Roman World, vol. 1. Leiden and New York: Brill, 1997.

Pohl, Walter, ed. *Grenze und Differenz im frühen Mittelalter*. Denkschriften/Österreichische Akademie der Wissenschaften, Philosophisch-Historische Klasse; Forschungen zur Geschichte des Mittelalters, 287. Bd. Bd. 1. Vienna: Verlag der Österreichischen Akademie der Wissenschaften, 2000.

Pohl, Walter, Johannes Krause, Tivadar Vida and Patrick Geary. 'Integrating Genetic, Archaeological, and Historical Perspectives on Eastern Central Europe, 400–900 AD'. *Historical Studies on Central Europe* 1, no. 1 (April 2021): 213–28, https://doi.org/10.47074/HSCE.2021-1.09.

Pohl, Walter and Helmut Reimitz, eds. *Strategies of Distinction: The Construction of Ethnic Communities, 300–800*. The Transformation of the Roman World, vol. 2. Leiden and Boston: Brill, 1998.

Pohl, Walter, and Helmut Reimitz, eds. *Grenze und Differenz im frühen Mittelalter*. Denkschriften/Österreichische Akademie der Wissenschaften, Philosophisch-Historische Klasse; Forschungen zur Geschichte des Mittelalters, 287. Bd. Bd. 1. Vienna: Verlag der Österreichischen Akademie der Wissenschaften, 2000.

Poskett, James. *Materials of the Mind: Phrenology, Race, and the Global History of Science, 1815–1920*. Chicago: University of Chicago Press, 2019.

Reich, David. *Who We Are and How We Got Here: Ancient DNA and the New Science of the Human Past*, 1st edition. Oxford: Oxford University Press, 2018.

Reich, David, Alkes L. Price and Nick Patterson. 'Principal Component Analysis of Genetic Data'. *Nature Genetics* 40, no. 5 (May 2008): 491–2, https://doi.org/10.1038/ng0508-491.

Ringbauer, Harald, Yilei Huang, Ali Akbari, Swapan Mallick, Iñigo Olalde, Nick Patterson and David Reich. 'Accurate Detection of Identity-by-Descent Segments in Human Ancient DNA'. *Nature Genetics* 56, no. 1 (January 2024): 143–51, https://doi.org/10.1038/s41588-023-01582-w.

Ringbauer, Harald, John Novembre and Matthias Steinrücken. 'Parental Relatedness through Time Revealed by Runs of Homozygosity in Ancient DNA'. *Nature Communications* 12, no. 1 (September 2021): 5425, https://doi.org/10.1038/s41467-021-25289-w.

Rodríguez-Varela, Ricardo, Kristjan H. S. Moore, S. Sunna Ebenesersdóttir, Gulsah Merve Kilinc, Anna Kjellström, Ludvig Papmehl-Dufay, Clara Alfsdotter et al. 'The Genetic History of Scandinavia from the Roman Iron Age to the Present'. *Cell* 186, no. 1 (January 2023): 32–46.e19, https://doi.org/10.1016/j.cell.2022.11.024.

Saag, Lehti and Mait Metspalu. 'Genetic and Geographical Origins of Eurasia's Influential Yamna Culture'. *Nature* 639, no. 8053 (March 2025): 46–7, https://doi.org/10.1038/d41586-025-00089-0.

Sarris, Peter. 'Viewpoint: New Approaches to the "Plague of Justinian"'. *Past & Present* 254, no. 1 (January 2022): 315–46, https://doi.org/10.1093/pastj/gtab024.

Schiffels, Stephan, Wolfgang Haak, Pirita Paajanen, Bastien Llamas, Elizabeth Popescu, Louise Loe, Rachel Clarke et al. 'Iron Age and Anglo-Saxon Genomes from East England Reveal British Migration History'. *Nature Communications* 7, no. 1 (January 2016): 10408, https://doi.org/10.1038/ncomms10408.

Sousa, Vitor and Jody Hey. 'Understanding the Origin of Species with Genome-Scale Data: Modelling Gene Flow'. *Nature Reviews Genetics* 14, no. 6 (June 2013): 404–14, https://doi.org/10.1038/nrg3446.

Speidel, Leo, Marina Silva, Thomas Booth, Ben Raffield, Kyriaki Anastasiadou, Christopher Barrington, Anders Götherström, Peter

Heather and Pontus Skoglund. 'High-Resolution Genomic History of Early Medieval Europe'. *Nature* 637, no. 8044 (January 2025): 118–26, https://doi.org/10.1038/s41586-024-08275-2.

Steinacher, Roland. *Rom und die Barbaren: Völker im Alpen- und Donauraum (300–600)*. 1. Auflage. Stuttgart: Verlag W. Kohlhammer, 2017.

Stock, Paul. '"Almost a Separate Race": Racial Thought and the Idea of Europe in British Encyclopedias and Histories, 1771–1830'. *Modern Intellectual History* 8, no. 1 (April 2011): 3–29, https://doi.org/10.1017/S1479244311000035.

Thomas, Mark G., Michael P. H Stumpf and Heinrich Härke. 'Evidence for an Apartheid-like Social Structure in Early Anglo-Saxon England'. *Proceedings of the Royal Society B: Biological Sciences* 273, no. 1601 (October 2006): 2651–7, https://doi.org/10.1098/rspb.2006.3627.

Tian, Yijie, István Koncz, Sarah Defant, Caterina Giostra, Deven N. Vyas, Arkadiusz Sołtysiak, Luisella Pejrani Baricco et al. 'The Role of Emerging Elites in the Formation and Development of Communities after the Fall of the Roman Empire'. *Proceedings of the National Academy of Sciences* 121, no. 36 (September 2024): e2317868121, https://doi.org/10.1073/pnas.2317868121.

Tian, Yijie, István Koncz, Norbert Faragó, Corina Knipper, Ronny Friedrich, Deven N. Vyas, Levente Samu et al. 'Unveiling the Complexity of Post-Roman Polity Formation Using Ancient DNA'. Preprint, *Evolutionary Biology*, 19 August 2025, https://doi.org/10.1101/2025.08.18.670760.

Trüper, Henning. *Topography of a Method: François Louis Ganshof and the Writing of History*. 1. Auflage. Historische Wissensforschung 2. Tübingen: Mohr Siebeck, 2014.

Vansina, Jan. *Oral Tradition as History*. Madison: University of Wisconsin Press, 1985.

Veeramah, Krishna R., Andreas Rott, Melanie Groß, Lucy Van Dorp, Saioa López, Karola Kirsanow, Christian Sell et al. 'Population Genomic Analysis of Elongated Skulls Reveals Extensive Female-Biased Immigration in Early Medieval Bavaria'. *Proceedings of the National Academy of Sciences* 115, no. 13 (March 2018): 3494–9, https://doi.org/10.1073/pnas.1719880115.

Velleius, Paterculus and A. J. Woodman, eds. *Loeb Classical Library*, LCL 152. Cambridge, MA and London: Harvard University Press, 2024.

Vida, Tivadar. 'The Migration-Period Countryside in the Former Roman Province of Pannonia'. In Irene Bavuso and Angelo Castrorao Barba, eds, *The European Countryside during the Migration Period: Patterns of Change from Iberia to the Caucasus (300–700 CE)*, 103–30. Berlin and Boston: De Gruyter, 2023.

Vida, Tivadar, ed. *The Frontier World: Romans, Barbarians and Military Culture*. Romania Gothica II. Budapest: Martin Optiz Kiadó, 2015.

Visy, Zsolt and László Bartosiewicz. *Hungarian Archaeology at the Turn of the Millennium*. Budapest: Ministry of National Cultural Heritage, Teleki László foundation, 2003.

Vyas, Deven N., István Koncz, Alessandra Modi, Balázs Gusztáv Mende, Yijie Tian, Paolo Francalacci, Martina Lari et al. 'Fine-Scale Sampling Uncovers the Complexity of Migrations in 5th–6th Century Pannonia'. *Current Biology* 33, no. 18 (September 2023): 3951–61.e11. https://doi.org/10.1016/j.cub.2023.07.063.

Wailoo, Keith, Alondra Nelson and Catherine Lee, eds. *Genetics and the Unsettled Past: The Collision of DNA, Race, and History*. Rutgers Studies in Race and Ethnicity. New Brunswick, NJ: Rutgers University Press, 2012.

Waldron, Tony. 'DNA in Bones'. *International Journal of Osteoarchaeology* 1, no. 2 (June 1991): 155–6, https://doi.org/10.1002/oa.1390010213.

Wang, Ke, Bendeguz Tobias, Doris Pany-Kucera, Margit Berner, Sabine Eggers, Guido Alberto Gnecchi-Ruscone, Denisa Zlámalová et al. 'Ancient DNA Reveals Reproductive Barrier Despite Shared Avar-Period Culture'. Preprint, *Nature*, 15 January 2025, https://doi.org/10.1038/s41586-024-08418-5.

Weale, Michael E., Deborah A. Weiss, Rolf F. Jager, Neil Bradman and Mark G. Thomas. 'Y Chromosome Evidence for Anglo-Saxon Mass Migration'. *Molecular Biology and Evolution* 19, no. 7 (July 2002): 1008–21, https://doi.org/10.1093/oxfordjournals.molbev.a004160.

Wickham, Chris. *Framing the Early Middle Ages: Europe and the Mediterranean 400–800*. Oxford and New York: Oxford University Press, 2006.

Williams, Matthew P. and Christian D. Huber. 'The Genomic Footprints of Migration: How Ancient DNA Reveals Our History of Mobility'. *Genome Biology* 26, no. 1 (July 2025): 206, https://doi.org/10.1186/s13059-025-03664-w.

Winney, Bruce, Abdelhamid Boumertit, Tammy Day, Dan Davison, Chikodi Echeta, Irina Evseeva, Katarzyna Hutnik et al. 'People of the British Isles: Preliminary Analysis of Genotypes and Surnames in a UK-Control Population'. *European Journal of Human Genetics* 20, no. 2 (February 2012): 203–10, https://doi.org/10.1038/ejhg.2011.127.

Wolfram, Herwig. 'Zur Ansiedlung reichsangehöriger Föderaten Erklärungsversuche und Forschungsziele'. *Mitteilungen des Instituts für Österreichische Geschichtsforschung* 91, nos 1–2 (1983): 5–35.

Wolfram, Herwig. 'Ethnogenesen im frühmittelalterlichen Donau- und Ostalpenraum (6. bis 10. Jahrhundert)'. In *Frühmittelalterliche*

Ethnogenese im Alpenraum, 97–151. Nationes 5. Sigmaringen: Thorbecke, 1985.

Wolfram, Herwig. *History of the Goths*. New and Completely rev. from the 2nd German edn. Berkeley: University of California Press, 1988.

Wolfram, Herwig. *The Roman Empire and Its Germanic Peoples*. Berkeley, Los Angeles and London: University of California Press, 1997.

Wolfram, Herwig. *Die Goten und ihre Geschichte*. 4. Durchgesehene und aktualisierte Auflage, Originalausgabe. Beck Wissen. Munich: C.H. Beck, 2022, https://doi.org/10.17104/9783406779114.

Wolfram, Herwig and Schwarcz, Andreas, eds. *Anerkennung und Integration: Zu den wirtschaftlichen Grundlagen der Völkerwanderungszeit 400–600: Berichte des Symposions der Kommission für Frühmittelalterforschung 7. Bis 9. Mai 1986, Stift Zwettl, Niederösterreich*. Vienna: Verlag der Österreichischen Akademie der Wissenschaften, 1988.

Wolinsky, Howard. 'Ancient DNA and Contemporary Politics: The Analysis of Ancient DNA Challenges Long-held Beliefs about Identity and History with Potential for Political Abuse'. *EMBO Reports* 20, no. 12 (December 2019): e49507, https://doi.org/10.15252/embr.201949507.

Y Consortium. 'A Nomenclature System for the Tree of Human Y-Chromosomal Binary Haplogroups'. *Genome Research* 12, no. 2 (February 2002): 339–48, https://doi.org/10.1101/gr.217602.

INDEX

The letter *f* following an entry indicates a page with a figure.